The Growing Tree

B. F. Wilson

The Growing Tree

THE UNIVERSITY OF MASSACHUSETTS PRESS

Amherst · 1970

TO NORM LAKE

Preface

THIS BOOK is intended for people, from the intelligent owner or observer of trees to the professional student of trees, who are interested in the basic processes of tree growth. It is not intended to be an exhaustive textbook. I have tried to present a picture of the processes that are characteristic of an entire growing tree and have made no attempt to cover processes in plant growth that are not in some sense peculiar to trees. The book is the culmination of more than ten years' work with growing trees so it is both a synthesis of my own work during this period and also a review of other people's work from my personal viewpoint. Much of the material was developed in connection with a course in tree physiology that I have taught for several years at the University of Massachusetts.

I am happy to acknowledge the support both of Harvard University's Maria Moors Cabot Foundation for Botanical Research and the Harvard Forest during much of my own research and the many contributions made to my ideas during discussions with Dr. M. H. Zimmermann, other staff members, and visiting scientists during my stay at Harvard.

Contents

Illustrations

The Growing Tree

Introduction

TREES FORM such a dominant part of our land-scapes, both rural and urban, that some under-standing of their formation and needs is a part of any understanding of life. Much of the interest in trees is practical or economic. Trees provide shade and windbreaks; they make a good architectural contrast with buildings; they may cover up foundations or screen off unpleasant views; they are the source of lumber, paper pulp, fruit, and many other tree-derived marketable products. On the debit side: they are blown onto power lines; their roots clog sewers; the leaves may drop off in the fall and have to be raked up and removed; they occupy acreage commer-cially more valuable when cleared. Still, in the balance, most people seem to like trees and want them in their environment.

Some of the interest in trees is more mystical than practical. Trees are so big and so old that they are often awe-inspiring. Perhaps as a carry-over from the days when—so it was thought —gods lived in or were trees, many people will admit to a re-ligious feeling when in the midst of a grove of trees with leaves arching high overhead. Trees that were living before Columbus arrived or the Mayflower or the observer himself, that served, say, to hang some unfortunate or somehow figured in past events can take on a special meaning. Many are preserved and documented with appropriate plaques. They are growing monuments to the past, and when they are cut, the study of their rings can be of historical relevance.[1] Trees have served long as literary metaphors, as dream symbols, as the subjects of myths. These mystical associations are difficult to define, but they are clearly important in our relation to trees and are probably the base of much of the impetus for the current conservation movement.

This practical and mystical interest in trees as they exist in the environment leads to a natural curiosity about how trees grow. The curiosity may be heightened by such concerns as your favorite tree dying, or by the necessity of speeding tree growth beside buildings or in a commercial operation, even perhaps in a desire to slow growth and produce dwarf trees. What may hinder the initial impulse to find out how trees grow is the fact that the growth increments in old, large trees are such a minute proportion of the vast bulk of the plant that they may be overlooked or taken for granted. Most people know that trees grow new leaves that eventually fall off, and that trees get taller and fatter and cast more shade as they grow. Most people also know that trees do not stretch; the stems and the branches grow longer, just at the tips, so that if you drive a nail into the trunk of a tree it stays at the same height above the ground rather than being carried upward as the tree becomes taller. Most people also know that the rings seen in the wood on the surface of a cut stump are annual rings and that if you count them you get a good estimate of tree age. They may also know that the width of a ring is related to how fast the tree was growing so that the wider the ring is the faster growth was. Beyond these points tree growth may seem hopelessly confusing. There are so many branches and leaves, so many annual rings, the stem is so big and the vast root system is all hidden under the ground.

A tree has thousands of branches and roots. Each one is somewhat independent on the one hand, but modified and regulated by all the other branches and roots on the other hand. Thus, a tree is a system of interacting components. There are not many different types of components, but there are a great many of each type. A useful approach to understanding a system like a tree is by the technique of model building, where each type of component is related in a causal or mathematical manner to the other. Models, such as flow charts or computer programs, are particularly helpful when considering a system like a tree, because a model which shows how some components are interrelated will hold for many parallel sets of components. The same basic model is simply used over and over. The beauty of this approach for professionals is that the tedium of repeating over and over the same process manually has essentially been eliminated by the modern high speed computer. For the amateur, it means that the hopeless confusion of a large growing tree can be resolved by understanding a few basic growth processes and the ways in which they are interconnected. A flow chart which tries to formulate the growth of a tree can be seen on page 130.

2
What is a Tree?

The Characteristics of Tree Growth

 A TREE is a special plant form, but it is basically like other plants. Trees use the same biochemical and cellular techniques as they grow and they obey the same physical laws as other plants. The differences in growth are not of a truly basic nature at the molecular or cellular level. It may be helpful to approach the problem of defining a tree by examining how trees fight in the struggle for the survival of the species. In plants, survival may depend on adaptations for increasing the amount of net photosynthesis. Without photosynthesis to produce energy in a useable form, the plant cannot stay alive or produce flowers and seeds. The solution to the photosynthesis problem that trees have "chosen" is to get their leaves higher than any other plants, and to keep them higher. Thus, trees are the tallest plants and they are perennial plants. Other types of plants have "chosen" other routes to survival. Vines climb up on other tall plants to get their leaves nearer the sun, but they cannot support themselves. Bamboos grow extremely rapidly to considerable heights, but then stop growing. Although the upright portion of a bamboo plant may live for more than ten years, bamboos are relatively short-lived compared to tree stems. One modern way to success in the evolutionary struggle is to grow fast to a relatively small size and produce many small seeds. This is the technique used by many small weed species. A surprising number of different plant groups, however, have developed tree forms to compete with

the other vegetation. The fossil record preserves the huge tree forms of plants like horsetails (*Equisetum*) and ground pine (*Lycopodium*) that we know today as relatively small plants, but that once formed the huge forests of the Carboniferous era.[1]

Any plant that attempts to become tall and perennial faces certain problems. The first problem is gravity. Most plants have "solved" this problem by developing the growth response of geotropism so that the stems grow up against the pull of gravity. Geotropism is certainly not peculiar to trees, however, and the mechanism will not be discussed here.[2] Geotropism is one of the first evolutionary steps that land plants made to get taller than other plants, but any plant that just keeps growing up soon faces the problem that it cannot support itself. The plant finally reaches a point where gravity, perhaps assisted by wind, wins out and the tree falls down. All tall plants have had to solve this problem by developing some mechanism to strengthen the stem.

The choice of materials is somewhat limited. Evolution of lignification of the cell walls, the process whereby the stem becomes "woody", may have contributed to the stiffness of tall plants, but the major modification to increase the strength of the stem has always been to increase its diameter. Over evolutionary time many different methods of thickening stems have occurred. The method used by trees is called cambial activity, the cambium being the tissue between the wood and the bark from which new wood is made, and a major part of this book will be devoted to various aspects of this method of adding new wood. Palms and tree ferns have methods for increasing the diameter of the growing point in the bud. Tree ferns have developed the clever adaptation of producing adventitious roots from the leaf bases. These roots grow down around the thin central stem and soon form a dense mat that strengthens the stem even though the strengthening is done by the roots.

Another mechanical problem that develops as the plant grows taller has to do with its need to be securely anchored in the soil. Trees again use the method of cambial activity to thicken the roots, especially near the base of the stem, so that they are strong enough to withstand the stresses from wind and the trees' own weight. Palms, which are certainly tall but will not be considered as trees in this book, have taken another approach to anchoring the stem and they produce more and more roots at the base of the stem rather than thickening the ones already present.[3]

As in most cases, the solution to one problem raises new problems that scarcely existed before. A feature of cambial activity is that there is a sheath of dividing, "meristematic" cells between the wood and bark that produces both new wood and new bark. The new wood strengthens the stem as it grows taller and as the load on the stem increases. As the tree grows in diameter through cambial activity and in height through extension growth, the area of the sheath of dividing cambial cells increases and each year more volume of wood is produced. Wood cells have thick walls, primarily made of cellulose and lignin, that confer strength to the wood. Cellulose and lignin are made from materials originally produced by the photosynthetic process in the leaves, a complex of materials, predominantly the common table sugar sucrose, that will be referred to in this book as "photosynthate." As the amount of cell wall produced increases, so does the amount of photosynthate needed to produce the walls. The inevitable consequence is that the tree must increase its total leaf area in order to increase the amount of photosynthate produced.

Modern trees adapted to the problem of producing more leaf area by producing branches that bear more small leaves. Although some tree ferns and palms branch, it is rather unusual and never so pronounced as in "real" trees. Palms and tree

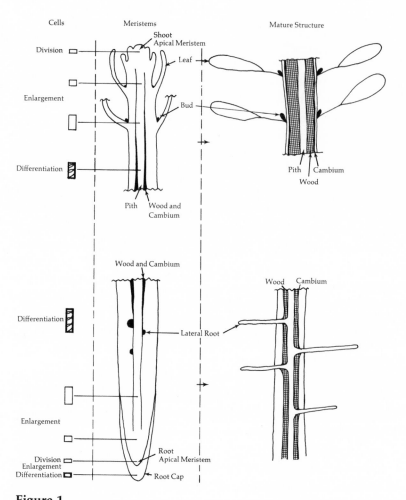

Figure 1

APICAL MERISTEMS

Each meristem has zones of cell division, enlargement, and differentiation; representative cell sizes are shown. The shoot apex produces lateral leaves and buds; the root apex produces a root cap and lateral roots.

ferns tend to increase leaf area by greatly increasing the size of the leaves that are formed. Their leaves are born in a tuft at the top of the stem and the intensities of mutual shading determine the maximum number of leaves that can be born on any one stem. A leaf requires a certain amount of light for photosynthesis. When leaves grow one above another the upper leaves absorb light and shade the lower ones. If there are three or four layers of leaves the light below them is not enough to support photosynthesis. The most efficient solution for the plant is to produce not more than three to four layers of leaves over the largest area possible. Branching increases the available area and more small leaves can be distributed more economically than a few large leaves. In fact trees have numerous mechanisms that regulate leaf orientation and survival on the basis of light intensity.

A tall branched plant must develop some mechanisms to control the pattern of branching so that the tree can attain greatest height by diverting nutrients to the central stem and so that the leaves born by the branches are in an optimum position to get adequate light to produce the food needed by the rest of the plant. Some trees maintain a single main stem throughout their lives, for instance the Christmas-tree sort of construction of many conifers. Other trees have only a relatively short single main stem and the upper part of the plant is broken into a number of more or less equally large branches as in oaks and many other deciduous species. The crown of a tree, the complex of leaf bearing branches that is supported by the main stem, must be so constructed that all the leaves get adequate light for photosynthesis and food production. Some trees solve this problem by keeping leaf bearing branches far apart so the light penetrates through the crown to leaves in the interior. Other trees produce a dense layer of leaves predominantly at the outer portion of the crown and the inside has no leaves. Whatever the distribution of leaves in the crown it is characteristic for a species of trees and it results from a strict control of the pattern of branching and leaf production during the development of the crown.

Two factors regulate the relative size of different branches and thus determine what will be the main stem and what will be the pattern of branching. These factors are, first, apical dominance, the inhibition by lower buds of buds above them, and second, the subsequent competition between the various branches of the crown. Both these factors have many variations and subtle interactions. Branching in a tree is complicated, and some aspects of the process will be discussed later.

As one might predict, increase in leaf area raises a whole host of new problems. Most plants face the dilemma that almost all gas exchange for photosynthesis occurs through specialized holes in the surface of the leaf called stomata. The dilemma is that as the carbon dioxide needed for photosynthesis diffuses in through the stomata, water is evaporating and moving out through them. The tree must have the carbon dioxide, but it also needs the water. Virtually all biological processes go on in a water medium. Water is essential for plant growth and survival, so the water lost from the leaves must be replaced by water taken up from the soil by the roots. As plants increase the surface area of leaves they increase the amount of water lost and thus have to compensate by increasing the amount of root surface area to increase the amount of water uptake.

Trees solve this problem by simply producing more and more roots in a process analogous to branching in stems. This technique of increasing root surface area is common to most plants, but trees have developed some special types of roots and special techniques of root production that will be discussed later. If the amount of water lost exceeds the amount taken up the water in the plant goes under tension and the plant is under "water stress," growth slows and stops and the plant may wilt.[4] Thus, as trees increase surface areas for water loss and uptake they must also increase the transport capacity of the stem to move the water from the roots to the leaves. The problem of transport capacity was solved very nicely by modifying cambial activity so that some of the wood cells are specialized for water transport and some for mechanical strength. Thus, the addition of new wood solves two problems—it strengthens the stem and it increases transport capacity.

Cambial activity also maintains the transport capacity of the highly specialized system that carries the food materials from the leaves to the growing roots and to the areas where new wood is being produced. This system, the phloem, requires living cells to function. Because phloem cells are relatively short-lived there must be a continual addition of new cells just to maintain the same transport capacity, and an even greater addition to increase capacity. An interesting point is that palms and tree ferns do not have cambial activity and do not have any method for increasing the transport capacity of their stems. Even if they had a method for greatly increasing leaf surface area, they would not be capable of servicing all the leaves by supplying water and removing the increased production of food materials, because their method of thickening does not increase transport capacity.

A final problem worth mentioning that is associated with the decision to become a tree is the problem of transporting materials over the great distances of a tree stem. Water and dissolved nutrients must move from the roots up to the leaves, sometimes more than 300 feet in opposition to the force of gravity, and the materials made by the leaves must move back down the stem and out to the growing roots. The problem of providing enough *channels* for movement has been solved, as mentioned, by specialization of some of the cells produced by cambial activity.

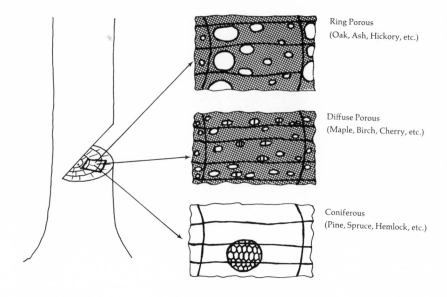

Ring Porous
(Oak, Ash, Hickory, etc.)

Diffuse Porous
(Maple, Birch, Cherry, etc.)

Coniferous
(Pine, Spruce, Hemlock, etc.)

Figure 2

MAJOR WOOD TYPES

In transverse section. Each piece has one annual ring (the boundaries are marked by the arcs of latewood). Lines running across the rings are rays. Large cells in the ring- and diffuse-porous woods are vessels; the cross-hatched areas around the vessels are composed of fibers and parenchyma. Coniferous wood is composed mostly of tracheids, some of which are illustrated, with no vessels or fibers and few parenchyma.

The problem of actual *movement* of material is solved no differently by trees than by any other plant, but the distances involved make these problems particularly acute. For instance the maximum height of trees may be limited, at least in part, by the water stress developed by pulling the water up to great heights.[4]

So we have touched on many points that can be used to answer the question "what is a tree?" First of all, there are many tree-like forms of plants and one of the least important problems is just exactly where the line should be drawn between trees and non-trees. A tree is a form that a plant develops to become one of the tallest, free-standing, perennial plants. For our purposes a tree has a single stem at the base, is much branched above, and has well-developed, long-term cambial activity. Nearly every group of land plants has examples of tree-forms, but we, somewhat artibrarily, will deal only with the angiosperms (deciduous trees, or "hardwoods") and gymnosperms (conifers in particular, mostly evergreen, or "softwoods"). Almost all examples will be from species or genera that are common in forests and parks of temperate climates of the Northern Hemisphere. It is somewhat unsatisfactory to put so little emphasis on trees of the tropics where genera that are only herbaceous in temperate areas have tree forms and where aspects of tree forms that are "normal" seem weird to those people used only to temperate zone trees.[5] The fact is that the bulk of research on tree growth has been done in the temperate zones of Europe and America, and my experience has been primarily in the temperate zone.

3

General Aspects of
the Growth Process

IT IS worth repeating that growth at the bio-
chemical and cellular level in trees is the same
as in other plants. Trees have cells that have
chromosomes to carry genetic information,
mitochondria to get energy from respiration,
chloroplasts to photosynthesize and the rest of the array of
cellular organelles that have been revealed by the electron
microscope. The path of cellular differentiation is regulated by
DNA through the type of enzymes that are produced in a cell.
The hormonal growth regulators presumably somehow interact
with this developmental system just as in other plants. The
details have not been worked out for tree species. In fact trees
are not very well suited for studies in genetics, biochemistry
and molecular biology. Scientists interested in solving these
types of problems want experimental organisms of known
genetic constitution that can be grown rapidly for many gen-
erations under closely controlled conditions. Trees, at least large
trees, meet none of these requirements. Thus, we have accepted
essentially on faith that the pathways and cellular control mechanisms worked out for other plants, sometimes even for micro-
organisms, also apply in trees.[1] In the few cases where these
cellular processes have been checked in trees, they appear to be
basically the same.

Trees produce most of their bulk—stem, branches, roots—
from meristems just as in other land plants. The concept and
operation of meristems will be discussed in detail below. Apical
meristems at the tip of each root and shoot produce the new

cells that result in elongation. Trees have more apical meristems than other plants because they have more roots and shoots. Although the meristems operate in the same way as in other plants, each apical meristem may modify the growth of the others, and simply because there are so many apical meristems in trees, the problem of apical meristem interaction is particularly complex in trees and important to their growth. The "lateral" meristem that produces the wood in trees, the cambium, is tremendously bigger in area than in other plants because trees are so big. What better place to study cambial activity than in the plants where there is most cambium? Trees being the tallest plants have special problems about the distribution of cambial activity to support themselves. At this sort of level the growth of trees begins to have a special, peculiar interest to scientists.

Tree growth is basically additive and cumulative. It is somewhat analogous to the growth of a savings account. The bulk of the tree can be understood as the principle, and growth may be in the form of annual increments that add on like annual deposits to each branch or root, or growth may be through producing new branches and roots, in this case the addition is like interest because the number added is a percentage of the number already there. Unlike bank interest this percentage is usually 200 to 1000 per annum or more, so trees grow a good deal faster than savings accounts. Death and loss of branches and roots and shoots can be compared to withdrawals from the principle.

Growth by meristems is simply additive. To carry the analogy even further it is like a Christmas Club savings account where there is no interest. Meristems are groups of undifferentiated cells that retain the ability to divide almost indefinitely. After each division, one daughter cell stays to perpetuate the meristem and the other passes through successive phases of differentiation before it finally is added to the fixed, dead mass of the tree.[2] Meristems may produce new cells at faster or slower rates, or for a longer or shorter time period each year, depending on environmental conditions, but these rates of increase are seldom more than 100% between years.

A model of this process would look like this:

Meristem division → cell → enlargement →

differentiation → cell death

One hundred percent differences in activity of a single meristem may seem pretty impressive. The really big increments in the growth of a tree, however, come about because of the increase in numbers of meristems growing (for apical meristems) or the increase in the area of the meristem (for the cambium). The number of apical meristems can increase exponentially, because every year each apical meristem may produce several new apical meristems that develop into the branch roots and shoots. The next year every new meristem can produce its new meristems and the number of branches and roots can increase at a phenomenal rate. Every year each apical meristem produces more cells to elongate each branch or root. The annual activity at any one point on the cambium may vary from year to year, just as the activity of apical meristems varies, and the annual amount is recorded by the annual ring width. Ring widths certainly vary a good deal, but as the tree grows the total amount of cambial activity over the tree is much more a function of the increase in the area of the cambium. The area of the cambium is increased in two ways. One way is the extension of the cambium into new roots and shoots as some of the cells produced by the apical meristems resume division and function as cambial cells. The other way is the mechanism, to be discussed later in more detail, for increasing the circumference of the cambium as the circumference of the tree increases due to cambial activity.

The history of annual meristematic activity is preserved in the tree. The width of the growth rings shows how much cambial activity there was in a given year. If the growth ring widths are analyzed up and down the tree it is possible to calculate the total volume of wood produced each year and to correlate cambial activity with weather conditions during a year or with some treatment, like fertilizing or thinning a forest stand.[3] In most cases thinning a forest stand, by removing some of the trees to let the remaining ones get more light, results in a marked increase in the width of the growth ring produced the following year. The annual length increments from apical meristem activity are marked in several ways. Each year when the buds open and the shoot grows out, the bud scales that serve as the protective covering of the bud soon fall off. The scars left on the stem where the scales come off are usually visible for several years and they can be used to mark annual length increments. In many trees, and pines are perhaps the clearest example, the annual length increments on older stems are marked by groups, or whorls, of large branches. In pines these branches develop the same year as the main stem just above them and in hardwoods they develop a year later. In either case it is possible to estimate the age of the tree by counting the number of groups, or whorls, of large branches. This technique is unreliable when the lower branches have fallen off and there are no scars left to indicate where they were or when the trees, like southern pines, produce more than one whorl of branches each year. It is also possible to work out increases in the length of the stem from the annual rings in the wood because the length of the stem that makes up each year's increment will have one less annual ring than the previous year's. The annual increments of roots are far harder to determine. There is usually no external marker like bud scale scars or whorls of branches. In many cases growth ring analysis can be

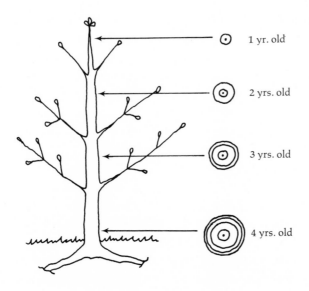

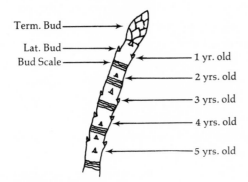

Figure 3

ANNUAL STEM INCREMENTS

Above, each annual length increment is marked both by whorls of branches and by a change in the number of rings in the wood. Annual diameter increments are marked by the rings. Below, annual length increments on twigs and small branches are marked by bud scale scars.

used to determine length increments. Unfortunately many growth rings in roots are discontinuous; they are crescents in cross section rather than rings, so it is usually not possible to determine the age of a root by counting the growth rings.

All the cumulative-additive processes must be superimposed on the life cycle of the tree. A tree, just as any other plant, must reproduce to keep the species going. Trees can reproduce either by flowering and producing seed, called sexual reproduction, or by asexual, vegetative reproduction, as when the broken willow branches from a tree take root along a river bank or as in the many propagating methods used by nurserymen. Sexual reproduction produces individuals of different genetic constitution because of genetic recombination during fertilization; vegetative reproduction duplicates in each individual the genetic makeup of the original plant, thus forming groups of individuals of identical genetic makeup. These groups are called clones and are common in trees that reproduce from buds from the roots, as in aspen, or from layering (rooting) of branches, as in black spruce. From the long-term evolutionary point of view sexual reproduction is more conducive to survival because it produces a varied population of individuals and this population is better able to cope with changing environments than a population of identical individuals. From a short-term point of view, either method may be effective in increasing the number of individuals of a species.

Much of the life cycle of a tree is similar to that of other seed plants. Seeds are formed and fall to the ground. The seeds may germinate immediately, as in the case of the red maple, but in many cases the seeds will not germinate until certain environmental conditions have been met. The most common condition required to overcome seed dormancy in temperate tree seed is a period of cold, moist conditions that is usually provided during a winter so the seeds germinate in the spring when the ground warms up. There are many other requirements—some seeds require light, some require dark, some require abrasion, or leaching. The problems of overcoming seed dormancy are fascinating and manifold. There are books that provide the empirical techniques necessary to make tree seed germinate and there have been a number of studies on the changes that occur in tree seed as dormancy is overcome by various treatments,[4] but basically these problems are problems of all plants, and are not limited to trees.

The germinated seed grows rapidly on stored material and develops into a relatively fragile seedling. The seedling stage is probably the most hazardous stage in the life cycle of a tree. Tremendous numbers of tree seedlings die from drying out, high temperatures, and animal browsing, among other factors. A forester or nurseryman is very concerned with methods to protect trees at this tender seedling stage. But again, all seedlings are tender and easily killed. Trees do not have it any better or worse than other plants.

It is not until a tree enters the phase of vegetative growth that it actually begins to be different from other plants, because it is here that the effort of trying to get above all other plants occurs. Most of this book will be devoted to discussing problems of vegetative growth in trees, the sort of problems that have been mentioned in the first chapter. One phenomenon that is marked in trees, but occurs in other perennial plants, is that there are two phases of vegetative growth. Most trees pass through a juvenile phase and then enter the adult phase.[5] During the juvenile phase they do not flower and usually reproduce more easily asexually. The leaves may look different from the adult phase. A fascinating example of changing leaf shape is *Eucalyptus perriniana* where the juvenile leaves are circular and born pagoda-like with the stem passing through the center of the blade, while the adult leaves are "normal" eucalypt shape,

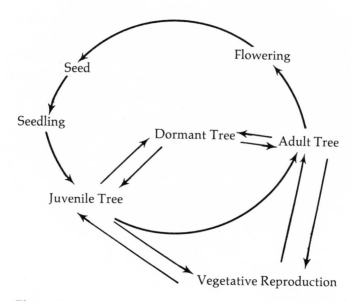

Figure 4

TREE LIFE CYCLE

This diagram is a modification of Dr. J. A. Lockhart's plant life "bi-cycle."

narrow, pointed at the tip and with a petiole. Leaves may be retained longer in the fall, as in the beeches. This juvenile phase is of variable duration, only a year or two in some trees and up to twenty or more years in others. In the adult phase the tree produces flowers that are pollinated and produce seeds and the cycle can start over again. Flowers may be produced abundantly every year, or only intermittently.

In most herbaceous species the life of a plant is terminated quite predictably. The plant flowers, senesces and dies. In these cases senescence and death involve fairly drastic changes that are initiated after flowering. Trees on the other hand do not enter senescence after flowering. Most trees are probably killed rather than dying from an internally triggered process of senescence. For example, the fast growing short-lived trees like gray birch and pin cherry that grow in open areas usually die when they are overtopped by taller longer-lived trees that shade the others out of existence. Certainly these trees can grow to respectable sizes and ages if they are not permitted to be overtopped. Striped maple is basically both short-lived and short in height; normally it is overtopped by other trees. Yet I have seen individuals so large that I could hardly recognize them. The question remains whether these trees are in any way "programmed" to die after a certain period or whether they are actively killed because they lack the capacity to become the tallest trees in a mature forest. Certainly the longer a tree lives the more likely it is to be killed by the environment—by the wind storms, lightning, floods, ice, fire, and the multitude of diseases that always seem to be in the process of eradicating some tree species or other. Even if the tree is not killed it may be sufficiently reduced in some attribute such as height, leaf area, root area, so that it cannot compete with other plants and is ultimately killed by competitive shading or drought conditions induced by more vigorous trees.[6]

Some trees manage to survive all these environmental vicissitudes; the best example is the bristlecone pine.[7] These trees may live to be more than 4,000 years old, so old that they even suffer from erosion from blowing soil and erosion is ordinarily a geological phenomenon. These bristlecone pines are impressive, because of their age, dramatic because of their wild twisted forms, but hardly forest giants. On the basis of our definition in the first chapter they might not be called trees at all. They are short, battered plants often with only a single strip of live cambium connecting the leaves and the roots. They also live under conditions which, although extremely arduous, high in the dry mountains, are virtually devoid of plant competition. They are the tallest plants where they live and can make good use of the few leaves they produce. The importance of these ancient trees to the present discussion is that they show no signs of programmed death. Those that survive for 4,000 years must be resistant to disease and capable of patching themselves up by producing vigorous new shoots even after the multitude of injuries that they appear to have suffered. Given freedom from outside threats, these trees appear to be immortal. We may ask whether other trees are not equally immortal, and simply less resistant or less adaptable after injuries, or else less fortunate in lacking competing trees.

In sum, all the growth of trees is by the production and growth of cells through the general process of meristematic activity, though the general process is subject to many modifications. If we are trying to distinguish among growing cells in a tree we need a number of different descriptions of the location of the cell. These are the questions we could ask: Which meristem are the cells associated with? Which phase of growth is the cell in? Which course of differentiation has the cell taken? And further we must ask: What time of year is it? What year? Where is the tree in its life cycle?

4
Form of the
Branch & Root System

 H. M. WARD summed up the material to be presented in this chapter when he wrote in 1909, "what a complex matter in its summation, but what a simple one in its graduated steps, the shaping of a tree is."[1] The whole branching system of a tree stem is called the "crown," and Ward was referring to the development of the crown of the tree. Crown form is a major part of the aesthetic appeal of a tree. Different crown forms can be used as a creative medium by landscape architects. It is the crown that produces most of the dramatic impact of a tree growing alone in a field or park. Deciduous species in winter reveal the intricate and complex patterns of the branches that bear the leaves. On a large tree there seem to be an astronomical number of branches, so many that it seems impossible to analyze the crown in terms of its parts instead of as a whole unit. Yet, this tremendously complicated structure has developed by the same sort of additive-cumulative growth processes that we have been discussing.

Before passing on to details of crown development it may be useful to survey some of the crown forms that commonly occur in trees. Young trees of most species have a central stem and a pyramidal crown. This pyramidal crown form is found both in young trees that eventually lose their pyramidal form, for instance oaks, as well as in those species such as pines, firs and spruces where the pyramidal form is often retained. The loss of the pyramidal form is usually caused by forking of the main stem and increased growth of some of the major branches so the crown of many mature trees is oval or egg-shaped, like those of the maples. When lateral branches grow outward and become relatively large, the oval of the crown becomes more and more flattened, like those of some of the oaks. As a tree begins to reach its maximum height the crown form begins to change again. The center of the crown slows down and the edges continue growing so that the top gradually flattens out. This flattening of the top occurs in most species as they leave the period of rapid growth associated with the oval or pyramidal crown form. Some old ash trees show particularly marked flattening and some species of pines are noted for the flat tops of the older trees. As trees get even older the crown begins to break up. Some of the large branches in the crown begin to die. This loss may be temporarily compensated for by the development from dormant buds of small "epicormic" branches along the trunk. The crowns of the tallest trees, the redwoods of California and the eucalypts of Tasmania, have this broken appearance that is sometimes called "stag-headed" because of the large dead branches in the crown. Perhaps the ultimate example of over-mature crowns are the crowns of the 4,000 year old bristlecone pines that have been discussed previously. These ancient crowns are mostly dead, but the occasional new shoot keeps them going.

We are most familiar with the crowns of trees during the mature stages before flat-topping begins. Unfortunately for owners of new houses, it takes many trees a number of years to pass out of the pyramidal juvenile crown form to the desired mature form. We have mentioned some of the form differences that are based on the outline of the crown, but there are many other differences between species. The conical shaped crown of conifers may vary from the broad-based crown of most pines to the nearly cylindrical shape of spruces, especially in far northern forests. Branches may incline up, or down, or frequently the branches go upwards at the top of the tree, horizontal in the middle and downwards at the bottom. The density and color of needles and leaves varies tremendously so that some oaks have a thin crown that can be seen through and others seem to be impenetrable. This list of differing characteristics could go on and on and each characteristic may make a tree more or less desirable for a particular use.[2]

Another class of differences in form is seen in species that are selected and propagated as horticultural varieties. Two interesting variations capitalize on extremes of branch angles. Fastigate varieties have all the branches pointing up and the crown is extremely compact. A lombardy poplar is a dramatic example of a fastigate crown. Fastigate varieties of many species are becoming more popular as house lots become smaller and there is simply no room for large spreading crowns. The other extreme is the weeping variety. In these trees the branches all hang down and the tree seems barely able to drag itself upwards. Weeping willows are common, weeping hemlocks and cherries are fairly common, but the most dramatic examples are the weeping beeches. Large specimens will cover a huge area making it possible to walk inside the crown, which cascades to the ground, so that it is almost like walking into a house or under a waterfall.

A further source of variation in crown form is the environmental conditions under which a particular tree is growing. The most common example of this variation is the difference between individual trees growing in a field or park, free from competition with other trees, and individuals growing in a forest stand where there is competition between the crowns of adjacent trees. In "open-grown" trees crowns achieve their fullest development. The outside of the crown is fully covered with leaves and the crown may reach to the ground. If the outer leaves are dense and absorb enough light the inner portion of

Figure 5

SILHOUETTES (I)

From left to right, above, palm, larch (deciduous conifer), elm;
below oak, maple.

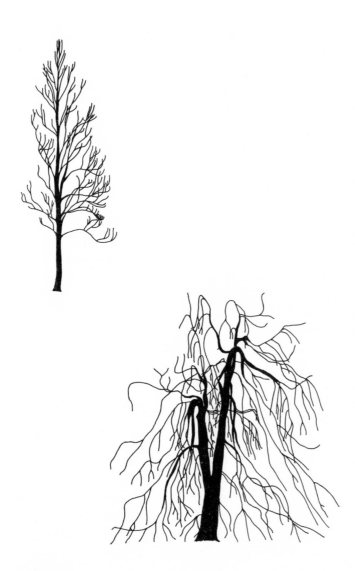

Figure 6

SILHOUETTES (II)

On the left a fastigate variety of a European linden, on the right a weeping variety of a European beech.

the crown may be devoid of leaves. If the outer leaves are scattered and pass a good deal of light then there may be leaves throughout the inside of the crown. In the forest where adjacent crowns touch to form a closed canopy of leaves, crown form is drastically modified. Leaves in the lower part of the canopy die because they are shaded by the upper leaves. Lower branches die if they do not bend upwards enough so that the leaves are out of the shade. Abrasion between branches of adjacent trees tends to break off the tips of lower branches. Thus, the leaf-covered portion of the crown tends to be limited to the portion above the point where adjacent crowns interlock and the lower portion is lost. Ovoid or spherical crowns become roughly hemispherical and the conical form of conifers is truncated shortly below the point of interlocking. Some oaks and pines are able to grow taller than the surrounding trees and then develop a widespreading crown that ultimately suppresses the adjacent shorter trees.

So far we have been treating the crown as a single unit. There may, however, be more than 20,000 branches in a mature red maple crown, and somehow this huge number of branches has proliferated from a single-stemmed seedling. How does the complex branching system develop?

From the discussion of meristems it is clear that proliferation of the crown must take place in some sort of exponential relationship. Each year each branch may produce new lateral branches. The following year the new branches in their turn produce more new branches. Obviously this process can lead to a very rapid increase in total number of branches. A likely form for this exponential growth is the allometric growth equation worked out by J. S. Huxley, and used by F. M. Turrell to describe the growth of grapefruit trees.[3] In this equation, $N = ca^n$, where N is the total number of branches, c is a constant for the particular tree, a is the age of the tree, and n is the exponential factor related to the number of branches added to each parent branch each year. Turrell has not calculated n for branch number but he has successfully used the equation to calculate leaf number for young trees. Presumably the equation would not work for older trees where the rate of loss of branches may equal or exceed the rate of addition of new branches.

Another equation or model which can represent the development of the crown is almost the same but is more flexible. This model is "iterative," which means that the simple mathematical process must be repeated over and over, once for each year, as the total number of branches builds up. In this sense the model is really closer to the actual way a tree grows because the tree itself is adding some branches each year. In this model, the number of branches added to the crown each year is a function of the number of old branches, i.e., those that were present the previous year (Nold), multiplied by the number of new branches added each year to each branch (n), with a figure for loss (L) subtracted. Thus,

$$Nnew = Nold(n) - L$$

One advantage of this model is that the values for n and L can be changed as the tree gets older, just as they actually change in real tree crowns. It is relatively easy to incorporate the changing values using a computer.

The simple iterative model is satisfactory on the level at which it operates. It is possible to generate reasonably likely values for the total number of branches by using appropriate values for n and L. The major trouble with the model is the gross oversimplification that assumes that all branches in the crown function in basically the same way as far as proliferation of new branches is concerned. There are two major exceptions to this assumption that merit discussion, and innumerable minor exceptions that serve further to complicate the process of branching in the crown.

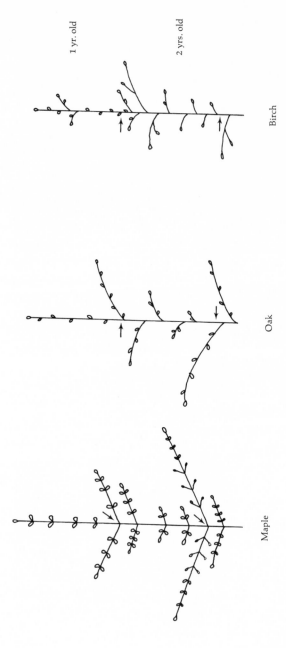

1 yr. old

2 yrs. old

Birch

Oak

Maple

Figure 7

BRANCHING HABITS

Branching habits of some different trees and the annual production of long and short shoots.

The first exception is that in most trees there are two classes of branches called "long-shoots" and "short-shoots." The distinction between these two classes of shoots is most marked in groups such as the larch, ginkgo and the Katsura tree (*Cercidophyllum*) where the short-shoots barely elongate each year. They bear leaves, but they do not branch, and often appear merely as little nubs along the long-shoots. In most hardwood species the distinction between short-shoots and long-shoots is not so clear-cut. Instead, most branches either elongate relatively little, do not branch, and are called short-shoots, or they elongate a relatively large amount, branch, and are called long-shoots. But there are intermediate branches that do not really fit in either category. Nevertheless, because most branches can be classified as short- or long-shoots, the concept remains very useful when considering the development of the crown.

Long-shoots bear lateral buds, some of which develop into more long-shoots and others into short-shoots. Short-shoots, on the other hand, bear lateral buds that are either completely inhibited and do not develop, or develop into flowers. The common example is that in apple trees most of the flowers are born on the short-shoots, often called "spur-shoots." As a result, there really have to be two separate models, one for long-shoots with the value of n being for long-shoots and one for short-shoots with the value of n for short-shoots and in both cases n is multiplied by the number of last year's long-shoots. The models must be separate because the n for short-shoots is so much greater than for long-shoots. I have estimated that in a mature red maple there are about 20,000 short-shoots and only 1,000 long-shoots.[4]

Shoots grow in a fairly consistent pattern. Red maple has a pattern that is common to many other hardwood species. Each year a long-shoot elongates. First all the leaves in the bud, the early leaves, develop and then more leaves, the late leaves, are produced. There is a lateral bud in the axil of each leaf, both early leaves and late leaves. These buds remain dormant until the following summer, and grow out when the terminal grows out. Therefore, the lateral branches are one year younger than their parent shoot. The upper laterals produce early leaves and late leaves and become new long-shoots. The lower laterals produce only early leaves, the leaves that were already in the bud, and these lower laterals become short-shoots. In a few species, for instance the fast growing gray birch in New England, lateral long-shoots may grow out in the same year that they are formed. This precocious growth appears to be more common in the southern United States.[5] Pines have a slightly different pattern. At the end of each long-shoot there is a group of large buds that grow out simultaneously to form the main shoot and its laterals, so that in pines the laterals are the same age as the parent shoot. In pines the little bundles of needles are really short-shoots. Ordinarily these short-shoots do not grow, but if the large buds are removed from a shoot the short-shoots of the needle bundles will begin to grow out to form new shoots.

The result of this pattern of long-shoots and short-shoots is that there are relatively few long-shoots bearing a great many short-shoots. The long-shoots grow out rapidly and form the framework of the crown, but most of the leaves (about 90% in red maple) are on the short-shoots that fill in the framework. There is sort of a distribution of labor among the branches in the crown, which means that the crown is able to enlarge rapidly but still maintain dense enough foliage to utilize the volume of the crown efficiently. As we shall see, the root system uses a comparable technique in exploiting the soil environment.

The second major exception to the assumption that all branches are the same is that lateral shoots, even long-shoots, are generally slightly smaller than the parent shoots and bear slightly fewer laterals than the parent shoot. Branches may be classified by orders. The main stem is the first order, laterals to the main stem are second order and so forth. As the order number of the long-shoots increases there is a general decrease in vigor noted above. Higher order long-shoots produce a lower proportion of long-shoots. In fact, usually by the fourth or fifth order, long-shoots bear no lateral long-shoots—only short-shoots. These short-shoots bear no laterals at all, so there are usually no branches higher than fifth or sixth order in the crown of a tree.

So, the model should be modified further, at least to break down the total number of branches into long-shoots and short-shoots, and to classify the long-shoots according to order. There will then be different n's and L's for short-shoots and long-shoots for each order of branches. These n values may be modified by the age of the tree, height of the tree or position within the crown, but theoretically it should be possible to develop a fairly realistic model for the growth of the tree crown. Differences for different species are accounted for by different values of n and L in the model.

Such a model would give a picture of how the *number* of branches in a crown changes as the tree grows; form, however, is dependent also on the position and length of the various branches. H. M. Ward formulated a simple, but useful, approach to modelling the change of form resulting from the position and relative length and thickness of branches by using silhouettes. He gave examples of how different mature forms could develop from a common pyramidal young form. For instance, starting with a pyramidal young stem with opposite branches, he shows how if the lower, "outwardly directed" buds develop the most vigorous branches the mature form is like maples and sycamores (*Acer pseudoplatanus*), while if the inner, upper branches develop the form is like that of a lilac bush. Ward gives other examples of the modification of form according to different patterns of branch development. For those interested in creating a model for this process, the limitations of his technique are that it is tedious to draw silhouettes and impossible to draw all the branches in three dimensions.

Representation of crown development in three dimensions would require a somewhat more complex model because it would be necessary to know the position of origin, the length and the orientation of each branch. The position of origin of each branch is determined by the distance between leaf nodes (the length of the internodes) on the long-shoots and by the pattern of long-shoots and short-shoots. Both lengths and patterns vary with order number of the long-shoot. The lengths of each annual increment for each shoot are a function of general tree vigor, order number and age of the branch. The orientation of the branch, essentially its branch angle, is complex and will be discussed later. Essentially, orientation is a function of the orientation of the original bud and the interaction of the magnitude of the geotropic response of the shoot with the weight of the shoot.

So, we have covered most of the step-by-step ingredients necessary for constructing a model of the development of crown form. The production of new branches can largely be predicted on the basis of branching pattern, elongation and orientation. The loss of branches is triggered by low light intensity from shading by other branches, and external factors such as disease, wind, snow or abrasion from other trees. Each one of these ingredients, or variables in the model, is simple enough in concept but the value for each variable changes with time, with position and with the general growth conditions of the tree. The important thing is to focus not on the seemingly limitless variation, but on the few basic processes that vary. These few processes are common to all species, varieties and forms grow-ing under all environmental conditions. It is the variation in these processes that produces the variations we ultimately see in crown form.

So far the discussion of form has been only about the form of the crown, but the root system also has a form. Unfortunately for the observer the root system of most trees is in the soil. The only time most people get to see an entire root system of a tree is when a tree is blown over by the wind and even in this case a very large part of the system has been broken off. Even for those people who study tree root systems professionally it is virtually impossible to see a whole root system. The most satis-factory technique to get an overview of a root system is to wash the dirt away with water. There are problems in this technique. Wet soil turns into mud and the mud must be removed, usually by using high pressures and large volumes of water on a slop-ing site. The high pressure means that most small roots are broken off and only the framework remains. There is a fairly clear-cut dichotomy in most root studies, either the larger woody portion of the root system is studied to get an idea of its extent and form, or the smaller roots (broken off and lost in the previous study) are investigated to study growth or water and mineral uptake. If one studies small roots it is usually done in such detail that only a minute portion of the root system is investigated and any sense of form of the whole system is com-pletely lost.

Just as in the crown (the shoot system), the root system undergoes changes with time, it varies between species, and within a species it varies between different soil conditions and different vigors of the shoot system. The root that emerges from the seed is called the radicle or primary root. The radicle is usually strongly geotropic and grows down into the ground. The first lateral roots do not develop until the first set of leaves is produced. Very early in the development of the root system differences between species become obvious. Early development may be related to the amount of reserve material stored in the seed. Large-seeded oaks generally have a very large radicle that grows down forming a carrot-like taproot with much smaller laterals. The radicle in maple, a medium-sized seed, is somewhat smaller. In relatively porous soil the maple radicle grows more or less straight downwards and produces laterals that are only slightly smaller than the radicle. In many environmental conditions the radicle does not grow downwards for very long. For instance, many seeds germinate within the moist year-old leaves on the upper surface of the forest floor. These leaves are only partially decomposed and usually offer enough resistance to root penetration so that the radicle grows horizontally between the layers of leaves, occasionally penetrating down between leaves, and the laterals are spread out horizontally between the leaf layers. In birch, which has relatively small seed, the first laterals often start to elongate and thicken just as much as the radicle. No root grows strictly downwards and it is soon impossible to detect which root is the radicle.

In the rocky soils of New England almost no trees have a distinct taproot for very long, but on sandy soils some species do develop a marked taproot. Despite the fact that most trees do not have taproots, the taproot is an important component of tree folklore. For some reason many people seem to think that underneath every tree is a large, carrot-like taproot that grows deeply into the soil. The fact is that most of the large roots in a root system of any tree grow more or less horizontally. These roots taper rapidly near the stem and then continue out with little or no taper, usually becoming at least as long as the tree is tall and in some cases considerably longer.

Oak   Maple   Birch

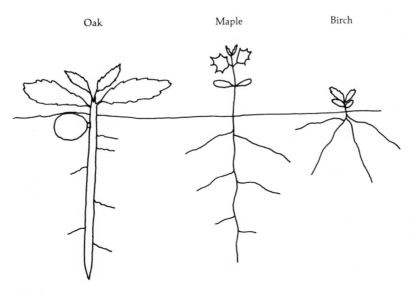

Figure 8

SEEDLING ROOT SYSTEMS

*The form is often related to seed size. Oak has a large seed,
maple medium, and birch small.*

Paralleling the long-shoot, short-shoot relationship in the
crown, in the tree root system there are a relatively few long
roots bearing numerous short roots. This type of "heterorhizic"
root system is common in trees, but not in herbaceous plants.
In some tree species the distinction between long and short
roots is fairly clear-cut, and in other species there are intermediate roots that cannot be classified as long or short roots.[6]
In general the short roots have relatively small diameter tips
which usually elongate less than a few centimeters, and usually
do not become appreciably woody. It is necessary to put in all
the "usuallys" when describing a root system, or for that matter

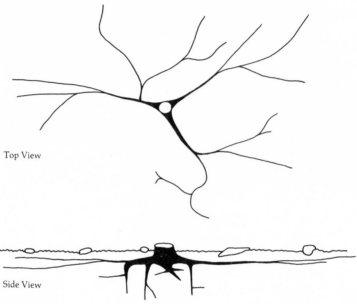

Top View

Side View

Figure 9

MATURE ROOT SYSTEMS

Diagram of the woody portion.

a shoot system, because there are exceptions lying in wait for every generalization. The important thing is to be aware of exceptions, but not to let their existence rule out the useful generalization that applies to most of the cases.

Some important features about the development of the root system are as follows. (1) Small roots can grow into large roots if the root tip diameter increases over a long period of time, but most large roots are produced lateral to pre-existing large roots under certain specified conditions. (2) Normally most long roots produce only lateral short roots; as usual there are exceptions such as oaks where laterals normally produced vary from short to long roots. (3) Large lateral roots are produced by parent large roots mostly when the parent root tip is injured, or in-active as in pines when the parent tip is entering or leaving dormancy. Thus, lateral long roots tend to be far apart and their spacing may be related to the frequency of injuries to the tip or to the annual periods of dormancy. (4) The lateral short roots may be extremely short and mycorrhizal, as in pine, or they may elongate somewhat and produce higher order laterals. In this case each successive order of roots tends to be smaller. A few orders away from the parent long root the tips do not produce laterals and may be morphologically identifiable as mycorrhizae. (5) Long roots can also arise adventitiously. In spruce after the deposition of a layer of soil following flooding new roots develop from the newly buried portion of the stem. These roots grow out and form a multilayered root system with one layer in the old soil and another in the flood deposited soil.[7]

Thus the number of roots in a root system develops much as does the number of branches in the shoot system with the major differences that short roots produce laterals and lateral long roots are usually produced only under specific conditions such as injury. It would be possible, however, to make a simple iterative model to predict the increase in the number of roots in a root system.

To understand a root system thoroughly it is necessary to know where each root is located in the soil. Thus, there have to be added the points of origin of laterals, elongation of each root, and, very important, the geotropic behavior of each root. A few roots in a root system have the "normal" geotropic response, such as the radicle, and grow downwards, but most (more than 90%) of the roots are either plageotropic, meaning that they grow at some given angle to vertical, or they may have no geotropic response at all and just grow in any direction. A large root system on rocky soils usually has few vertical roots, while on sandy soils these may be many. In both cases the verticals are close to the stem. Root geotropism will be dealt with in considerable detail in a later chapter. At this stage it is only necessary to realize that it is the geotropic response, or

Figure 10

WARD'S SILHOUETTES
Silhouette models reproduced from H. M. Ward, Trees V. Form and Habit *(Cambridge University Press, 1909). Figure numbers start on page 70 for figures showing form development. Starting*

lack of it, which determines how many roots in the system grow downwards, how many horizontal, etc. It is also presumably some aspect of geotropism, perhaps modified internally or perhaps modified by local soil environment, that determines the depth of the horizontal portion of the root system. This depth is characteristic of a given species. For instance, oaks usually have a relatively deep horizontal root system, a foot or more below the surface, whereas maples and birches have most horizontal long roots within six inches of the surface.

So, if the values for variables in root system development are known it is theoretically possible to make a model that will cover development of any root system on any soil. The practical problem is that almost no values for the variables for any species are known. In a few species the process by which variables operate has been described, but seldom quantitatively. The ultimate model would generate values for each variable from local soil conditions, temperature, moisture, density, etc., from the hormonal status of each root tip, and the internal level of nutrition. How some of these factors may operate to influence the variables in root development will be discussed later.

---

with alternate (above) or opposite (below) branching in young pyrimidal trees, different patterns of branch development result in different forms. Above, if a few laterals develop and outward buds are favored it is like some lindens (Ward fig. 37), if laterals de-velop equally and new laterals develop at the tip of the parent axes it is like willow and poplar (Ward fig. 35), if there is outward curvature and almost pendant branches it is like a wych elm (Ward fig. 38). Below, if more vigorous growth of **inwardly** *directed buds and if the tips stop so that the laterals grow out forming dichotomies you get lilac (Ward fig. 29), if more vigorous growth of* **outwardly** *directed buds you get maple (Ward fig. 27), if downward and outward growth with recurved tips it is like horse-chestnut in the open (Ward fig. 31).*

5

Elongation and Dormancy of
the Branches and Roots

THE NEXT FEW chapters cover in more detail the processes, and the regulation of the processes, that contribute to crown development, elongation, lateral formation, and finally orientation of the laterals. As in almost any growth process, the division into these separate phases is merely for analytical convenience because in actual fact all the processes proceed simultaneously and all are interrelated. Hopefully, their interrelation can be shown later in a model. In each chapter the process will be talked about first in the shoot system and then in the root system. Again, this is an artificial and somewhat misleading division made solely to simplify the discussion. Try to bear in mind that not only are all the processes proceeding simultaneously, but the whole plant usually grows at once. The shoots provide materials required for root growth and the roots provide materials required for shoot growth. As a general rule, an isolated root or shoot system does not survive unless new roots or shoots are regenerated to make a whole plant again.

This first chapter in the series is about elongation, and the discussion really covers two quite separate aspects of the process. The first is the actual process of elongation of a shoot or root. How much does it elongate, what is the process, and what regulates the amount of elongation? This growth part of the process determines the rate at which the root and shoot systems are extended into new areas of the environment, while the relative amounts of elongation of different types of branches and roots determines the pattern and efficiency with which this new environment is exploited. The second aspect of the process is physiologically regulated dormancy. This process is the active cessation of growth, usually associated with some structural changes to the root or shoot, that makes it more resistant to adverse environmental conditions. This cessation of growth is considered active because there is an actual change in development upon entering dormancy, rather than a passive cessation such as might result from exhaustion of food reserves. Both of these processes are vitally important; elongation must occur to permit further exploitation of the environment, and dormancy must occur—at least in temperate climates—to avoid loss of meristems by freezing or desiccation.

Elongation

Shoots and roots elongate from cell elongation. It is not the *division* of cells that is directly responsible for elongation; division of a cell does not cause an increase in volume because the combined volume of the two daughter cells is the same as the volume of the parent cell. But cell division is indirectly responsible for elongation because cells have a limit to which they normally elongate and thus total length is the product of cell number and cell length, and total elongation is the product of cell number and the difference between final cell length and initial cell length.

In shoot elongation, and in leaf growth which occurs slightly before, but at almost the same time, the process of cell division and cell elongation are often separated in time, particularly in trees that form buds. In bud formation new cells are formed by cell division in the shoot apex; these new cells enlarge a little bit with enough differentiation occurring so that there are recognizable leaves in the bud. These leaves are usually fairly well formed with the major teeth of the margin already developed. The process of bud formation begins in the early summer and usually is finished well before autumn, so the compressed shoots with stem and lateral buds all overwinter inside the bud scales. The next spring the leaves begin to grow rapidly as the buds swell and "break," and then the cells in the internodes elongate, so that elongation of the shoot occurs. During the rapid spurt of growth following bud-break most of the growth is from elongation of cells that were formed by cell division the previous year.

Thus, in those species that produce leaves only in buds, the maximum amount of elongation is predetermined by the number of cells produced the previous year, assuming that there is some maximum cell length that is not exceeded in normal growth. Pines are good examples of such predetermined growth. All the needles and virtually all the cells of the stem are present in the bud; a new bud is formed even before the current elongation is completed. For this reason the elongation of pine shoots is partly regulated by environmental conditions of the previous year, when cell division was occurring, and partly regulated by conditions of the current year when elongation is occurring. Many pines have developed a modification of the basic plan of forming buds annually. Fast growing pines, especially those growing in the south, frequently go through multiple bud flushes during one growing season. A bud grows out in the spring and a new one is formed; this new one may not stay resting until the next spring, but may grow out during the same year and then a third bud is formed. Some pines may flush three or more times in one year. Both hardwoods, particularly oaks among others, and softwoods, such as pine, will flush a second time if the tree is vigorous and if the weather in the later part of the summer is especially suitable for stem growth. This second, irregular flush of growth is called lammas growth, if it is the terminal shoot, and prolepsis if it is lateral shoots.[1] Prolepsis and lammas growth may occur separately or together. Multiple flushing, lammas growth and prolepsis all have profound influence on the crown of the tree. The influence is detrimental if a late flush of growth goes too far into the autumn and the new growth is killed by frost. These growth habits are really just variations on the basic separation between cell division and cell elongation with dormancy conditions determining the conditions under which a bud will break and start growing.

Continuous shoot elongation without bud formation would be courting disaster when the autumn comes. An example of extended elongation with simultaneous division and elongation is the growth of stump sprouts after the main stem has been felled for timber. The stump sprouts originate from rudimentary buds buried in the bark or, in some species like beech, a new shoot differentiates from the callus tissue that develops at the cut surface of the cambial area. These new shoots then grow extremely rapidly; in some cases they continue to grow until the newest growth is finally killed by the frost. Virtually all of this growth is from elongation of cells currently produced by cell division. The "naked" buds in the axils of eucalyptus leaves are also buds that appear to be able to undergo unlimited growth by combined cell division and elongation. Undoubtedly there are tropical trees that show the same type of growth with no bud formation.

Many trees, like maples, poplars, birches, have well defined buds that break in the spring as the preformed early leaves grow out. Just as in pines, division and elongation are separated. These early leaves grow out rapidly and internode elongation lags slightly behind leaf development. Then, after a short pause in leaf development, late leaves are produced.

These late leaves are often morphologically distinct from early leaves. They are produced during the current season, and the internodes between them begin elongating rapidly as the leaves grow. In production of late leaves there is no separation of division and elongation. In these trees with early and late leaves, short-shoots generally produce only early leaves and long-shoots produce both early and late leaves.

The differences between long- and short-shoots appear to be due to differences in growth regulators in the two shoot types. The two regulators that are most commonly associated with the stimulation of cell and shoot elongation are the auxins and the gibberellins. Most research has been done on the auxins, particularly the older work, and most of that work was done on herbaceous species. More recent work shows that both gibberellin and auxin are required for cell elongation but the work on short- versus long-shoots has emphasized auxins exclusively.[2] The general conclusions from these investigations are that short-shoots are deficient in auxin, and that in long-shoots the amount of auxin is low until the late leaves are produced. The implication seems to be that the early leaves just do not produce much auxin and therefore there is very little internodal elongation because auxin is required for elongation, but the late leaves produce a relatively high amount of auxin and there is proportionally greater elongation in shoots with late leaves. Gibberellins are also produced by leaves so it may be that early leaves produce relatively small amounts of gibberellins as well.

There are other variations in shoot length, less drastic than those associated with long-shoots and short-shoots, connected with the different orders of shoots. In general, the first order long-shoot, the main stem, grows fastest and successively higher order long-shoots grow slower. There are several possible reasons for this decrease in length with increased order which is observed in all tree species. One is that there is some

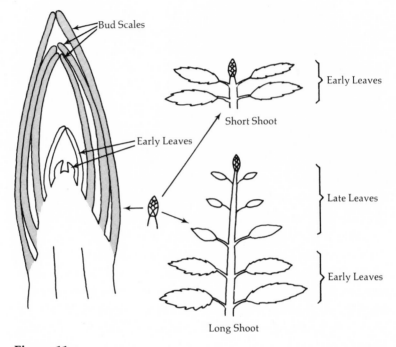

Figure 11

LEAF PRODUCTION

Early leaves are present within the bud and develop on all shoots.
Late leaves are produced after the bud develops and usually they
are produced only on long shoots.

sort of apical dominance, that somehow the apex of the parent shoot can effectively reduce the amount of auxin in the lateral long shoot and thus reduce its elongation.[3] Another possibility is that the various orders of shoots are competing with one another for available carbohydrates and the older, larger parent shoot has the competitive advantage just because of its size.

There is some reason to consider the second possibility even though it seems natural to expect that each individual shoot produces its own photosynthate and therefore there is no direct competition between different shoots. In fact it has been shown that until the shoot becomes self-sufficient its growth is dependent on stored materials. In deciduous trees carbohydrates stored in adjacent young shoots are utilized, while in conifers most of the reserves are in the old needles, particularly the previous year's needles. The usual way to obtain such information is either to remove portions presumed to be storing reserves, for instance the needles in pines, or to separate storage areas in deciduous trees by girdling,[4] to see whether the removal of a source of supply affects subsequent growth. There is ample evidence that movement of food materials through the phloem goes from where it is stored (the "source") to where it is being used (the "sink") and the direction of flow is determined only by the relative positions of the storage and use. Thus, it is quite possible that materials stored in a lateral shoot could move out of that shoot and into the parent shoot if the parent shoot started growing sooner, or if the intensity of its growth was such that it used more material, representing a greater sink. If the terminal bud starts growing slightly sooner than the laterals, then the lateral shoots may be off to a bad start with the first leaves smaller and the whole growth of the shoot slowed. Another factor might be that the lateral shoot that loses out in the initial competition for stored material is then more liable to be affected by apical dominance from the terminal bud.

The annual elongation of shoots varies from year to year, but there is also a general pattern of variation over time. The main shoot starts growing in height quite slowly until a large leafy crown has developed, then it grows rapidly for a long period of time, but, as it approaches its maximum height, annual height increment begins to decrease. One major factor that may be involved in the decrease in growth with height, and indeed may be one of several major factors in determining the maximum height of the tree, is that as the height of the tree increases the water stress increases. Cell growth can occur only through the uptake of water as a result of the osmotic pressure of the cell; therefore, if water stress can become great enough to counterbalance the osmotic pressure, cell elongation cannot take place. This might happen at maximum height and as water stress increases with height it may be a significant factor in the reduction in height growth observed in taller trees.[5]

One source of water stress is the fact that water has to be moved against the pull of gravity. This tensile force increases at the rate of one atmosphere (14.7 lbs/in^2) for every 30 feet of height. Therefore, in the top of a tree 90 feet tall there is a pressure of -3 atmospheres even in the pouring rain if the pressure at the base is zero because the water hangs there. When the water starts moving as the leaves transpire, it takes additional force to overcome the resistance to movement of water through the vessels in the wood. The force required to overcome this resistance is of the same magnitude as that required to overcome gravity, so the stress at the top of the 90 foot tree is approximately doubled, to -6 atmospheres, when water is moving. All these calculations are assuming that there is adequate water available to move into the tree. Under drought conditions water stress develops even at the roots of the tree, but it is always higher at the top of the tree due to resistance to flow and the effect of gravity. A -6 atmosphere stress at the top of a tree may reduce cell elongation and reduce shoot elongation compared to what it would be at zero water stress. If under drought conditions the stress at the roots begins to approach −9 atmospheres, then the stress at the top of the 90 foot tree would approach −15 atmospheres and −15 atmospheres is just about the wilting point of plant tissue. This is the amount of stress that actually pulls water out of leaf cells causing them to wilt. Cell elongation stops well before wilting, so droughts during the period would reduce elongation and cause a shorter than normal annual increment. In fact, it has been shown that most elongation occurs at night, when water stress is lowest, because there is little or no transpiration, water movement through the soil can reduce water stress at the roots, the column of water is no longer moving, and stress is not great enough to completely inhibit elongation.[6]

As a general rule, every long-shoot, like every main stem, has decreasing annual elongation with increasing age; the main stem grows less with increasing height, while branches grow less as they increase in length. The result is that crowns often tend to become more or less cylindrical towards the bottom because the lowermost branches are the longest and are elongating extremely slowly, while the upper, younger branches are elongating fairly rapidly. This pattern is most obvious in conifers, but less obvious, although present, in deciduous trees. There are also marked differences between species in the amount the branches grow in diameter relative to the main shoot in both length and diameter. Spruce branches are relatively small in diameter while in many oaks upper branches become as large as the main stem. In fact the process of relative branch enlargement is one of the major factors influencing the form of the crown.

It seems safe to presume that increase in length of a shoot and increase in diameter are connected somehow, perhaps merely because more increase in length means more leaves, more photosynthate and thus more cambial activity. In any case, the main stem appears to dominate the growth of the laterals in some species though not in others. A number of mechanisms may be involved. One may be apical dominance. Somehow the main shoot regulates, reducing in most cases, the level of growth substance in the laterals, particularly auxin, and therefore growth is reduced. This mechanism is postulated for the inhibition of lateral bud growth, but it is a little difficult to extend it to the growth of lateral shoots where the apex of the lateral may be several meters from the main shoot. For the same reason, it seems unlikely that competition between shoots for reserve carbohydrate is very effective when the lateral shoots are so long. A third factor is that the lateral branches are growing at an angle. They are not growing vertically. The regulation of this angle is complex and will be discussed in a later chapter. When organs are growing out of their preferred orientation to gravity, there is usually a reduction in elongation. This reduction is called "geotonus," and seems to affect the actual elongation of the cells. Therefore one would predict that the more nearly horizontal a branch is the greater would be the reduction in elongation. An additional factor is that the more nearly horizontal a branch is the more likely it is to have reaction wood formation. Reaction wood formation may operate on reserve materials and thus actually compete with the elongating cells within the same branch. In sum, the mechanism for progressively decreasing growth rate in branches is not clear, but it must be related to the complex of factors that distinguish a branch from the main stem, and once that distinction is unclear as in oaks when branches become indistinguishable from the main stem, it becomes impossible to calculate the relative decrease in growth rate.

The elongation of roots occurs through the same general meristematic process as the elongation of shoots. Cell division is followed by cell elongation, but in roots there is no structure like the bud in which a great many small cells are stored in preparation for rapid elongation in the future (although lateral shoot buds may develop on older roots in some species). As a result, cell division and cell elongation generally coincide in roots. The relative rate of elongation is usually well correlated to the diameter of roots; thus the large root tips 1 to 3 mm in diameter may elongate 1 meter a year and small root tips less than 0.5 mm in diameter may elongate only a few centimeters in a year. The longest roots elongate faster than the shoots so the longest roots are usually 1.5 to 2 times as long as the tree is tall. Just as in shoots, the amount of elongation tends to decrease with increasing order number, and probably the annual elongation decreases as any root gets longer.

Many problems about root elongation are really parts of the basic problem of how much root elongation is controlled by materials moving down from the stem and how much it is controlled by materials produced by the root tip itself. Ultimately just about all materials used by the root except those absorbed from the soil must come from the stem, but the root has some synthetic capacity of its own. For instance, most of the nitrogen that is absorbed as nitrate by the root is converted into organic nitrogen, such as amino acids, within the root and moves up in that form to the shoot. There is also mounting evidence that the root system, and this presumably means the root tips, can synthesize its own growth regulators, in particular gibberellins and cytokinins, and that these move up to the shoot.[7]

Most experiments using small trees, seedlings or young cuttings, show that root elongation is directly and very closely related to photosynthetic activity of the leaves. For instance, if the leaves are removed from first year seedlings, root growth stops almost immediately. If the leaves of cuttings are put in the dark, root elongation slows with only a short time lag. On the other hand, observations on larger trees show that root growth is often more or less independent of shoot growth. For instance, observations in root cellars where the root tips can be viewed through glass walls show that in the spring many species begin root growth before shoot growth, and in the fall most species continue root growth long after shoot growth. In those species that start before shoot growth the general impression is that the roots grow when soil temperature is high enough, usually above 4°C (38°F). Supporting evidence for this statement is that roots that were kept heated all winter, even though the crowns were frozen in the New England winter, kept elongating all winter. In fact when a long woody root was cut off several meters back from the tip the root tip continued to elongate for several weeks. Root tips on long woody roots may also start growing in the spring even though the root is severed from the stem.[8]

Because these results differ in different size trees, it may be that size actually accounts for the difference. The roots of little plants are so close to the leaves and so dependent on currently produced material that they are probably extremely sensitive to anything that affects the leaves. As the plant grows larger the materials have to move farther to get from leaves to roots, there are more storage materials than can be utilized and the roots are essentially buffered from the shoots. This does not mean that root growth is not regulated by shoot growth; it does mean that the response is slow and small variations in elongation are probably more due to local conditions around the root such as temperature and moisture than to variations in the environment of the tree crown.

Root elongation is obviously dependent on photosynthate from the crown, but it is not very clear what growth regulators are required. It has been difficult to grow tree roots in sterile culture, but for many plants successfully grown in culture there has been no necessity for adding auxin, gibberellin or cytokinins to get good root elongation. Added auxin generally inhibits root growth, as does added cytokinin; added gibberellins seem to have little or no effect. The reason could be that, as mentioned, the root tip can synthesize its own required growth regulators, and therefore added regulators become supraoptimal.

If root tips produce their own regulators this could explain why larger roots grow faster than smaller roots. They may simply have more growth promoters so they grow faster, therefore attracting more photosynthate to enable them to grow even faster. Perhaps the growth regulators, particularly cytokinins, actually create a sink—as they have been shown to do in other systems—and thus more photosynthate moves to the roots. The same reasoning on competition between root tips for available photosynthate would apply here as it did with competition between shoots. The decrease in elongation with distance from the stem does not happen until the roots are many meters from the stem, if indeed it occurs at all, and if it does it would seem logical that the mere factor of distance over which the carbohydrates must be translocated would be enough to decrease growth.

There are a number of reports in the literature that the longest roots occur in the poorest soils or from the poorer trees. In addition the trees on the better sites have more frequently branched root systems. It is difficult to explain why a non-vigorous tree, with less photosynthate to go around, should have longer roots. The answer may lie in the observation that these roots are less branched. If in the vigorous trees the available photosynthate is distributed evenly among many competing root tips, then no one root may become very long, while in non-vigorous trees, branching is infrequent so the few large root tips get the lion's share of the available photosynthate.

Another problem which is related to elongation is that root tips can become larger over time, even changing from small to large tips. This increase may occur in the radicle and also in lateral roots. Because diameter and elongation are related, these roots then begin to elongate more rapidly. Why should root tips get larger over time? Why do just some of the tips get larger? These are questions that have no definite answers, but there are some likely speculations. Presumably both increase in diameter and elongation are dependent on the general nutrition level of the root apex. If the level is high, the tip can increase in diameter and elongate a great deal. In the seedling, leaf area is quite low; the whole existence of the plant is somewhat marginal with current photosynthate being used primarily to increase the leaf and root system. Judging from studies of root: shoot ratios, the shoot has priority for photosynthate at this early stage.[9]

Thus, it may be that the seedling gradually builds up its general nutritional level until finally there is enough available photosynthate so that some is used to increase the diameter of some tips. Presumably, following the general hypothesis that root tip size is related to growth rate, the biggest tips will have the competitive advantage for materials and begin to increase in diameter. In some species, like birch, where there are several equally large tips in the seedling root system, they all begin to enlarge. In a true taprooted seedling, like oak, presumably most of the available material is used up by the taproot and the laterals stay small. As the root system develops the large tips always have the competitive advantage and are most likely to be the tips that increase in diameter.

Dormancy

The process of dormancy is a determining factor in elongation because entering dormancy terminates elongation and elongation cannot begin until dormancy is broken. There is a whole terminology of dormancy based on the treatments necessary to break dormancy. Romberger has discussed these problems in detail.[10] The function of dormancy is to create some sort of resistant structure so a meristem can survive cold or dry periods. Most of the complex requirements needed to break dormancy appear to be designed to insure that dormancy will not be broken too early during an only temporary period of favorable environment.

The dormancy structure in the shoot is the bud. The bud consists of external protective bud scales and internal, partially developed leaves. Both bud scales and leaves differentiate from leaf primordia formed on the flanks of the shoot apical meristem. Bud scales are really just modified leaves. In fact, under some conditions it is possible to get appendages halfway between leaves and bud scales. Bud formation results from a complex sequence of events involving reduced internodal elongation and a switch from leaf to bud scale production, then back to leaf production. As the shoot enters dormancy and begins to make a bud, these appendages develop into modified leaves called bud scales, and internode elongation stops so that the scales are very closely grouped on the shoot. These scales arch over and cover the tip of the shoot while there is a reversal in appendage differentiation and the primordia produced after the scales develop into preformed early leaves. Then, finally, activity stops and the bud is complete and ready for winter.

Bud formation does not stop the formation of leafy appendages, but it does shift their course of differentiation. In shortshoots the appendages produced after the early leaves develop into bud scales, while in long-shoots they develop into leaves. The critical difference is not cessation of appendage production, but appears to be in switching the pathways of differentiation. This complicated process of bud formation is usually initiated early in the summer, well before there is any chance of cold weather, in a sense anticipating the probability of drought periods in late summer. Not all branches on a tree form buds at the same time. For instance, red maple short-shoots may form buds a month before the long-shoots. Usually these buds remain dormant until the following spring, when all buds break dormancy largely at the same time. In some cases, as previously mentioned, there are multiple flushes of growth, including lammas and prolepsis, in which the bud is broken during the same season it is formed. Usually this breaking is associated with warm, wet, late summers.

The physiological regulation of bud formation and dormancy is complex; it differs from species to species. Dormancy must be initiated by some environmental signal that precedes periods of hostile environment. The least variable of such signals is day length, or photoperiod. In many species elongation is rapid during a long-day photoperiod and slows, leading to bud formation, when the tree is grown on short photoperiod. Obviously photoperiod is not the only regulator of dormancy or all the buds on a tree would go dormant at once. Entering dormancy may also be triggered by cold weather or water stress. Whatever the environmental signal to enter dormancy, the change in environment itself cannot cause the elaborate changes associated with bud formation. The environment must affect some factor which in turn switches cells into different patterns of differentiation. A recent study of this mechanism was done by Eagles and Wareing[11] on birch. They found that on short days elongation stopped and a bud was formed, while on long days elongation and leaf formation continued. They made an extract of mature leaves under short days and found that the extract would induce bud formation in trees growing under long days. The active substance in the extract was isolated and tentatively identified as abscisic acid, a growth inhibitor. Pure abscisic acid applied to the bud would induce bud formation in birch seedlings even while they were growing under long days. Thus there is a nice circle of evidence to suggest that the environmental signal for bud formation in birch is the shortening days of summer. Under short days the leaves begin to produce large amounts of abscisic acid which move to the apical meristem and cause the shift to bud scale formation. This type of response to short days is presumably common in trees. In other cases, for instance pines, where no leaves are produced that were not produced in the bud, bud formation may begin automatically while elongation of the cells in the previous bud is going on. In these cases there may be no requirement for an environmental stimulus, except for the stimulus that permits buds to break.

The opening of the buds in the spring may have a photoperiodic requirement that is met by the increasing day length in the spring. There is presumably also a temperature requirement. The very fact that most trees show genetic differences in the timing of bud opening within a species suggests that there is some receptor mechanism for an environmental stimulus that is different from a simple physical or chemical phenomenon such as the increased rate of reactions with increases in temperature. Many buds have a chilling requirement. They require a period of cold treatment during which, if it is at all comparable to breaking dormancy in seeds, an inhibitor is broken down and a promoter or promoters such as gibberellin or auxin builds up. In most cases this chilling requirement means that a bud will not undergo lammas growth, but many chilling requirements can be overcome by high light intensity and high temperatures. They can often be overcome too by the addition of gibberellins to the dormant bud. There seem to be several possibilities in lammas growth. One is, as stated above, that the warm, late summer conditions overcome the chilling requirement, and the other is that in trees that frequently have lammas growth there is a progressive dormancy that is easily broken at first, becoming increasingly difficult to break the longer the bud is dormant.

Roots may also go "dormant," although their dormancy is different from dormancy in shoots. They do not produce an elaborate structure comparable to a bud, but many roots do undergo anatomical changes associated with stopping growth and these changes presumably make the roots more resistant to adverse conditions. Certainly, if a growing root is suddenly subjected to freezing temperatures the tip usually dies, whereas the adjusted "dormant" roots can survive subfreezing weather. One thing that many people do not realize is that below freezing soil temperatures are rare even in severe winter climates, if there is an insulating layer of snow or leaves and no permafrost. There is no question that soil does freeze, particularly in exposed areas, and that roots must survive this hazard if the tree is going to survive, but the incidence of freezing temperatures in the soil is less frequent than might be expected.

The best studied type of dormant structure in roots is the "metacutized" layer that forms in pine root tips. Most tips, however, merely turn brown after becoming dormant, as the outer cells fill with suberin. Since it is obvious that brown tips are dormant, it is often assumed that all white tips are growing. Unfortunately, tips of some species never turn brown, and in most species suberization lags behind the cessation of dormancy by a week or more. Mycorrhizal root tips stop growing and become covered by a mantle of fungal hyphae. When tips start growing again after a dormant period they grow right out through whatever dormancy structure is present, so often the point where the tip stopped elongation is marked by a ring of different colored tissue on the surface of the root.

Wilcox has studied the metacutized "markers" that show where red pine roots have been dormant.[12] He finds that smaller roots, growing near the surface of the forest floor may stop and start growth a number of times during one summer, while the largest roots may grow throughout the whole summer. The same sort of thing has been observed in maple roots where constrictions, that usually mark mycorrhiza, may form during each drought period in the growing season. Wilcox shows that this starting and stopping of root tips is what accounts for the often reported bimodal curve for root growth. Many investigators have stated that roots elongate in the spring and in the fall, but hardly at all during the summer when stem growth is most rapid. This midsummer pause could be due to competition between the shoot and the root system, even to the inhibition of root growth by the high auxin produced during active shoot growth, or it could be due mostly to the fact that where bimodal growth is observed there is a period of summer drought. This drought would only have to be in the litter to cause a significant reduction in the proportion of growing tips that was measured in a sample during the summer lull. Whatever the cause, it seems that a midsummer decline in the number of growing roots does occur. In investigations of individual large roots growing under well watered conditions there was no such midsummer decline. This observation might suggest that the decline is not really related to the growth of the shoot system, but rather to the fact that transpiration is greatest during that period and it may induce drought conditions which have more effect on the small than on the large roots.

It is not at all clear what conditions are required to make roots resume growth after they become dormant. It may simply be a resumption of warm, moist conditions or there may actually be chilling requirements, etc. There are just not enough observations about root dormancy to come to any conclusions.

Thus, the actual amount of elongation of a branch or a root in a certain year may be a function of many different factors,

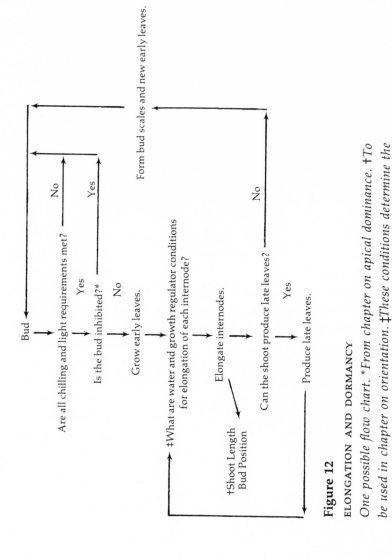

Figure 12

ELONGATION AND DORMANCY

One possible flow chart. *From chapter on apical dominance. †To be used in chapter on orientation. ‡These conditions determine the rate of elongation and, thus, the final internode length.

all modified by the overall nutritional status of the tree. The size of the organ appears to be a factor, for generally speaking, the bigger the bud or root is the greater the elongation, both because big organs represent larger sinks and because the larger the bud of predetermined shoots the larger the number of cells that subsequently elongate. Apical dominance may regulate elongation, by inhibiting directly or just by regulating competition between organs. The environment is important both overall, by speeding or slowing growth processes (probably if the environmental conditions are poor the larger organs grow relatively more than when conditions are optimal because the larger ones have the competitive advantage) and locally because roots that get too dry stop growing and shoots that are shaded will be less able to support leaf growth and will produce smaller buds.

There seem to be instances where root elongation and shoot elongation are independent. For example, they seem to occur at different times according to the bimodal curve of root growth. There are also instances where they are dependent on each other, as, for instance, when girdling a tree kills the roots and then the shoot dies too, but if the roots are kept alive by root grafts with other trees then the shoot also stays alive. It seems probable that any apparent independence of root and shoot growth is due to the buffering ability of large trees and could not occur in small, seedling trees.

6
Lateral Formation and
Apical Dominance
Production of New Branches and Roots

 THE VAST MAJORITY of new buds are formed as lateral buds in the axils of leaves or bud scales. (The axil is the upper angle between the stem and the petiole of the leaf.) There are a number of alternative fates for these new buds in angiosperms. In the temperate zone, most of the lateral buds that are formed are actually present in the terminal bud in the axils of early leaves. They overwinter in a terminal bud, spend another year dormant in the axils of the mature leaves and finally grow out in the third summer. Buds in axils of late leaves usually grow out the summer after they are formed, but some may grow out during the same summer. This precocious growth ("syllepsis") occurs in rapidly growing gray birch in New England, more frequently in a number of southern species and is fairly common in fast-growing stump sprouts of many species.[1]

Some buds do not grow out for many years, if at all. These are the buds in the axils of bud scales and some of the lower buds on long shoots. These buds may eventually grow out to form epicormic branches after injury to the shoot. Although they are called "dormant," they do grow a little bit each year, thus keeping from being buried in the wood, and they also produce new scale-like appendages. Not only do they elongate slowly, but they may also branch, multiplying the number of dormant shoots under the bark. This multiplication is particularly obvious at the base of birch trees where the buds can be

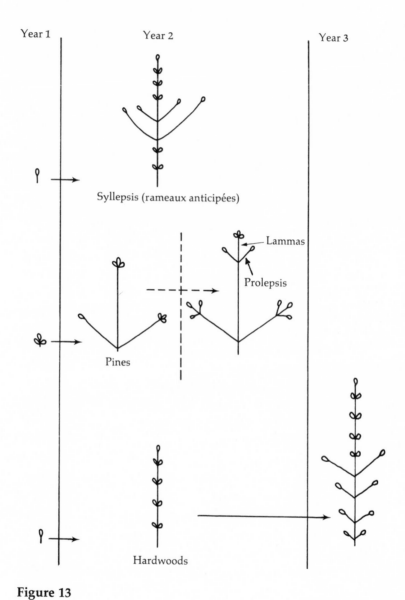

Figure 13

BRANCHING

Different patterns of apical dominance and apical control.

clearly seen, but it occurs in maples, pines and probably many other species. The increase in number of dormant buds accounts for the tremendously prolific sprouting of such trees as red maples.

Pines produce two sizes of buds. Lateral buds in the terminal bud develop into tiny short-shoots bearing the needles. A few large lateral buds are produced at the tip of the shoot and develop into full size shoots, usually only slightly smaller than the terminal shoot, and form the whorls of branches. The number and size of these large laterals is roughly proportional to the vigor of the shoot. Normally the short-shoots of pines (the needle fascicles) fall off after a year or so without even elongating, but sometimes they will grow out into recognizable shoots. I have observed this in the upper fascicles when a long cold spring was suddenly broken by a warm spell, and also after experiments in which all the large buds and any new shoot growth were removed from young pines. In pines kept disbudded almost all the short-shoots of the fascicles may eventually start growing.

Why do some of the buds in hardwood trees remain dormant for varying lengths of time? In some cases the mature leaves appear to inhibit lateral bud growth and if they are removed, experimentally or by insect defoliations, the laterals in their axils grow out. Under normal conditions the leaves fall off in the autumn and the laterals are free to grow the following summer, but then they do not all grow out evenly. The general pattern is that the terminal bud and the upper laterals grow the most, forming long-shoots, and shoots farther down the stem grow less so that the lower ones form short-shoots. The terminal bud scarcely inhibits the upper lateral buds, but the upper buds do inhibit the lower ones. If the upper lateral buds are removed before bud break, then the ones below, which are now the uppermost surviving buds, grow out into long-shoots even though under normal conditions they would have been short-shoots. There is definitely some sort of regulation of the growth of lower shoots by the upper shoots, but there does not seem to be any complete inhibition such as is suggested by the term "apical dominance." All the buds grow out, but some elongate more than others. In pines all the large buds, formed at the end of the previous summer, grow out even though none of the fascicle buds grow out under normal conditions. Again, there is no sign of apical dominance in the sense of completely inhibiting lateral bud elongation as in many herbaceous plants. The term "apical control" has been suggested for this regulation of relative elongation.[1]

Some buds are, however, inhibited in the classical sense of "apical dominance." These are the dormant buds, most commonly those in the axils of bud scales. As long as there are active buds above them they do not elongate any more than necessary to keep up with diameter growth of the stem. If the upper buds are killed by fire or cut off in a logging operation, then the lateral buds grow out to form either sprouts, if they are near or below ground level, or epicormic shoots if they are higher up the stem. This is quite consistent with the classic experiments on apical dominance by Went and Thimann in the 1930's. To a limited extent the application of auxin to the upper portion of stem will maintain the inhibition even though the upper buds have been removed. The obvious conclusion is that auxin moving down the stem somehow interferes with the growth of the bud; there will be more about this later.[2]

Although most lateral buds are formed in the axils of leaves, bud scales, or cotyledons as a normal aspect of the production of lateral appendages by the shoot apical meristem, lateral buds may also form on the roots of such species as aspen, beech, sweetgum (root apical meristems are *never* converted to shoot apical meristems). Buds can also differentiate from callus tissue formed after wounding, as they do in some cases from the cambial area of beech stumps. Roots may also develop from callus tissue. Whether roots or buds develop has been shown under experimental conditions to depend on the ratio of two growth regulators. If there is high auxin and low cytokinin, roots usually develop and if there is high cytokinin and low auxin, then shoots develop.[3]

Buds in roots may also be inhibited in the classical sense, but there is some disagreement. Usually root buds of aspen or sweetgum will start growing if the stem is cut or injured. The inhibition can be partially restored by applying auxin to the stem end of root cuttings in aspen, thus suggesting that it is at least to a degree an auxin regulated inhibition. But there are also observations and experimental evidence which show that the aspen root buds start growing just because of high soil temperatures even though the stem is uninjured. Of course the effect of high temperature could actually be to lower the effective amount of auxin moving from the stem. In sweetgum, there are also observations showing that local soil conditions can affect root bud growth. For instance, in a tree growing at the edge of a field the root buds on the roots growing into the field grew out, but the root buds on roots in the forest did not.[4]

A recent explanation of how inhibition of the classical type works is from the investigation of Sachs and Thimann on peas.[5] Their conclusion was that lateral buds were inhibited in the first phase by low cytokinin. They were able to release buds by adding cytokinin which presumably started activity in the apical meristem of the lateral bud. This activity of meristematic cells is associated with production of auxin and the auxin causes elongation of the internodal cells that leads to elongation of the lateral shoot. They could obtain slight, but measurable, elongation by adding auxin directly to the lateral bud, thus causing internodal elongation without apical activity. The initial release by added cytokinin was only partial and the shoots would soon stop growing again, but the growth after release could be prolonged by addition of gibberellin to the growing lateral. Thus, the terminal was still doing something to inhibit the laterals even after the lateral had started growing. Apparently the terminal was inhibiting auxin and gibberellin production by the laterals. Apical dominance appears to be a good example of the interaction of several classes of regulators in a growth process.

So far we have described two types of inhibition, one by mature leaves, the other by terminal buds, but why do some buds grow out in spite of the presence of mature leaves and terminal buds? This type of release is usually associated with rapid growth as in stump sprouts or the example of the fast growing gray birch. These laterals may grow because the rapid use of auxin during the growth lowers the amount reaching the lateral buds and weakens apical dominance. These "rameaux anticipées"[6] always seem to be from the axils of late leaves so the buds have not overwintered. There is very little delay in their outgrowth. They apparently develop and grow out without passing through a period of inhibition, without ever forming an actual dormant bud.

In the most common type of apical dominance in temperate zone trees, all the dormant buds on a shoot, the laterals and the terminals, grow out at once. There is no inhibition of the first phase of bud break; the second phase starts in all the laterals but is soon inhibited in all except the uppermost laterals. The number of upper laterals that develop into long-shoots is correlated to the "vigor" of the parent shoot. A fast growing tree may have four or more long laterals develop on parent long-shoots, while a slow growing tree, or branch, may have two or fewer. A comparable sort of relationship has been found in herbaceous plants by several investigators. The general finding is that "vigorous" plants have less apical dominance, are more branched, than plants that are shaded or somewhat deficient in minerals and therefore are not very vigorous.[7] Part of the explanation for this phenomenon could be that the faster growing plants are more subject to producing "rameaux anticipées," but another good possibility is that in vigorous plants competition between buds is not so severe because there is more nutriment to go around. Thus, in branching of a non-vigorous tree the buds at the top get the jump on the others and soon draw on all the reserves for their elongation. These buds then go on to produce late leaves and become long shoots; the lower ones never produce late leaves and stay as short shoots.

The next question, then, is, why do the upper buds grow better than the lower buds anyway? The experiment of removing the upper buds and getting long-shoots from the lower buds that are now uppermost shows that there is nothing inherently different in the upper buds; it is a positional effect. The factor most likely to give an advantage to upper buds is the polar transport of auxin, one of the most important regulators of tree form development, although in no way peculiar to trees. Of the growth regulators only auxin has polar transport. What "polar transport" means is that auxin produced by apical meristems and leaves moves predominantly down the shoot, away from the leaves. This direction is called basipetal—towards the base of the shoot. Gravity has only a very slight effect on polar transport; inverting a shoot does not significantly affect the direction of transport. Various investigators have shown that the direction of polar transport is basipetal in the stem, but in the root system auxin is transported toward the root tip.[8] Thus auxin is transported from the shoot tip to, or at least almost to, the root tips. As will be seen, it is a rather important point whether or not the shoot auxin goes all the way to the root tip or whether the root tip produces a little bit of auxin that moves toward the shoot tip for a short distance before it is swamped by shoot tip auxin and the polarity is reversed.

What polar auxin transport means to suppressing growth of lower buds is that the auxin concentration gradually increases down the stem as more and more growing buds are contributing. Thus, whatever the inhibiting influence of auxin is, it would be expected to be greatest towards the base around the lowermost active buds. Once the lower laterals begin to be inhibited, the growth rate slows, they cannot compete for photosynthate and they soon form a bud.

All in all the situation of apical dominance is very complicated in trees. There seem to be all kinds of combinations of bud dormancy—apical dominance, apical control, and competition between uninhibited buds. The response of buds appears to be related to bud age; to whether or not they have overwintered; to bud position along the shoot; to bud size in determining competitive ability. Success in bud competition appears to be modified by the general vigor of the tree.

The regulation of lateral formation and growth is just as important, and just as complicated, in the root system as in the shoot system. Formation of lateral roots usually occurs somewhat back of the root tip, the distance roughly proportional to the rate of elongation of the tip and up to 8 cm in rapidly elongating long roots. The new lateral root primordia develop internally from pericycle cells. If the root tip is injured, lateral tips may form just back of the injured portion either from pericycle, if they have differentiated, or from undifferentiated cells. If the root is injured far enough back from the tip so that it is woody, then the new primordia adjacent to the injury often develop from callus tissue, or phloem parenchyma, usually opposite the large rays that are associated with the protoxylem.

There are also adventitious roots that form on the stem. Adventitous roots are usually fast-growing, long-roots. In some species these roots develop from preformed groups of initial cells that are present in the stem, as, for instance, in many of the poplars and willows that are noted for easy rooting. In other cases adventitious roots develop from callus tissue, if there has been an injury, or from secondary phloem tissue. Adventitious root formation is the basis of rooting cuttings for vegetative reproduction either artificially or naturally. Artificial rooting of stem cuttings is a standard technique for propagating tree species. Usually juvenile trees root more easily than adult trees and in many cases the base of the cutting has to be dipped in auxin. The requirements differ from species to species, for instance willow branches root in plain water, and there are several books specifying the requirements.[9] Adventitious roots also form on some species, for instance, black spruce, when the soil level is raised due to deposition of silt during flooding. The new roots develop in the stem where it is newly buried and they grow out into the new soil. Some species, again black spruce is a good example, form new roots when the branches are covered with soil, or even when they are just kept moist and dark. This is also a technique used to propagate some plants, called layering, and it can occur naturally. The result is that a single tree can gradually spread out through layering of the branches as each branch develops into a new tree and in turn produces new branches.

A type of root that is fairly common in moist tropical or sub-tropical areas is the aerial root. These roots start adventitiously from branches, or, in the case of strangler figs, they grow down from the seedling which has germinated in some crevice on another species of tree. The aerial root tips are sometimes extremely large—5+ mm in diameter. The aerial hanging tips may grow down through the air to the soil and then thicken and act as supports for the branches.[10] In this case they are serving a mechanical function usually performed by the stem.

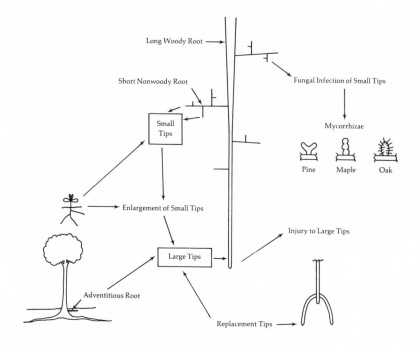

Figure 14

ROOT SYSTEM DEVELOPMENT

A diagrammatic model where the key processes are (1) the initial development of large tips, and (2) the proliferation of large tips (that form long roots) and small tips (that form short roots).

Perhaps the most basic aspect of the pattern of growth of root systems of most trees is that some tips are relatively large and grow fast, eventually forming the woody framework of the root system, and most of the root tips are relatively small, elongate relatively slowly and form most of the absorbing surface of the root system. It is the small, slowly growing roots that are most likely to be infected by fungi to form mycorrhizae. Seedling root tips are all small, but, in a vigorous seedling, within a few years the largest, fastest growing of the seedling root tips enlarge in diameter and become the "large" tips. The problem of classifying root tips into groups by size or morphology or some other characteristic has more than once caused investigations into tree roots to degenerate into an argument over semantics. The problem exists because there is always a continuum out of which artificial groups are separated, for instance many root tips are clearly relatively small or relatively large, but there are plenty of intermediate ones. A complicating factor is that a root tip may undergo size changes of several hundred percent even during one season. So the classification of large and small tips is not proposed as the answer to the taxonomy of root tips, but is rather a convenient way to identify most of the tips in a root system at any point of time. There may, or may not, be any parallel with the physiological classification into "feeding" or "absorbing" roots that is usually attached to the mass of small roots. Undoubtedly most of the absorbing is done by the small roots because there are so many more of them, but there is no reason to think that the large roots do not also absorb water and nutrients even if their total contribution to the tree is insignificant.

Some of the big root tips come from enlargement of small root tips, but this is not enough to account for the numbers observed in a root system. Large tips usually produce small lateral tips. Occasionally, however, large tips develop lateral to large tips, reminiscent of the relation of short-shoots to long-shoots in the crown. These large tips grow out rapidly, thicken, and cause a branching of the woody root. Another source of large tips is from adventitious roots which may start right out as large tips. In both these cases the new root starts big rather than growing big, so the first aspect of apical dominance in roots is what regulates the initial size of a new lateral root.

There are several conditions under which new lateral roots will be large roots. In all cases they are formed lateral to large parent roots. Most frequently they form when there is an injury to the parent tip. If a few millimeters or centimeters of the parent tip are eaten by soil organisms, crushed or removed experimentally, then new large tips develop just back of the injury. Usually more than one tip forms and as they grow out they produce a branching of the woody root. This reaction to root tip injury seems to be general among temperate zone trees and is a major cause of branching in these trees. Wilcox has· observed that in conifers large lateral tips may also be formed when the parent root tip has just entered or is just leaving a dormant period.[11]

In both these cases it seems that when the apex of a large root is active then small lateral roots are formed, but when it is inactive, dormant, or removed then large lateral roots are formed. This can be interpreted as a form of root apical dominance. The presence of the apex does not inhibit the formation of laterals, but it does inhibit the formation of large laterals. Most research seems to suggest that lateral root primordia are formed in response to auxin moving down from the stem.[12] Removing the auxin source in tree seedlings by taking off the leaves stops lateral root formation.[12] Unfortunately, most work on lateral root formation has been done on herbaceous material that does not form such markedly different sized root tips, indeed does not form large tips at all. Therefore, there are no data about the effect of different treatments on lateral root tip size.

A reasonable hypothesis seems to be that when the root tip is intact the effective auxin concentration at the point where laterals are initiated is relatively low because the tip somehow interferes, perhaps by producing an inhibitor.[13] In any case, when the tip is removed the effective auxin concentration may be raised and polar auxin transport now extends to the very end of the root. Conditions of nutrition are good because the large tip is a big sink. Finally, only the large tip is physically capable of producing a large diameter lateral. Under all these conditions large diameter tips are produced. If several large tips are produced then they may compete between themselves and presumably the largest tip would be the most successful and therefore form the main part of the root. If the tips are nearly identical so that there is no competitive advantage, then there may be a number of equal sized branches as is frequently observed.

The regulation of lateral root size in adventitious roots does not involve any considerations of apical dominance, but it must be related somehow to the internal environment of growth regulators and required growth factors. The initiation of the primordia in the first place requires high auxin, moist conditions and, in some cases, the process is inhibited by light. The requirements vary widely between species and many species do not seem to have a high enough endogenous auxin concentration to permit root formation under natural conditions. Easy rooting species require only dark, moist conditions, for instance for layering and adventitious root formation in black spruce. One common way to induce a locally higher auxin concentration is to girdle, or even sever, a stem so that as polarized auxin transport continues, the auxin builds up at the basal end of the cutting or on the upper side of a girdle. Girdling, or breaking off of "cuttings," can certainly occur under natural conditions too, and then roots may form in species that would not root by such a simple process as layering.

7

Orientation of Laterals

Direction of Branch and Root Growth

 ANY MODEL of root or shoot system develop-
ment, whether it is an informal set of silhouettes
or a formal model adaptable to a computer,
requires some information about orientation.
Branch lengths and numbers are not enough
because the tree grows in three dimensions. The tree is exploiting a three dimensional environment and has adapted its development to do so efficiently.

In the beginning orientation is no problem. After the seedling
germinates the new shoot grows up and the new root grows
down. But this simple situation does not last long. The shoot
usually continues upward but the root, the "taproot" that
grows out of the seed, often stops growing completely or bends
and grows off laterally. The problem of orientation becomes
complicated as lateral roots and shoots are formed.

The first factor determining the orientation of a lateral is its
point of origin. A bud which forms high on a tree will grow
into a branch whose base, at least, is high in the tree. A corol-
lary is that if the orientation of the parent organ changes, for
instance a change in branch angle as a branch gets older, the
orientation of all the laterals from that parent also changes. On
windy days the orientation of the parent and lateral branches
may change very rapidly resulting in a real competition for
space with abrasion and breakage of competing branches.

Once the place of origin of a lateral is determined, the direction of elongation is the second factor determining orientation.
Organ elongation occurs through cell elongation. Oriented

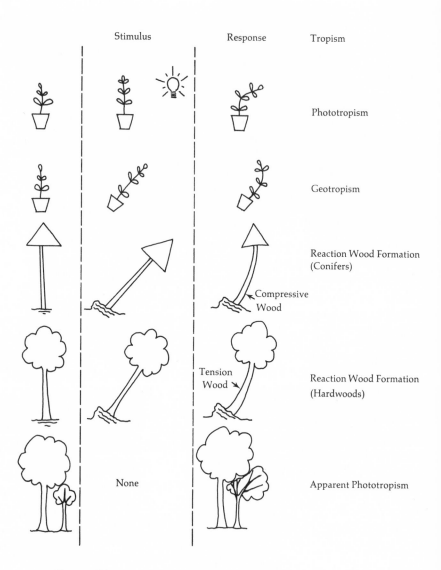

Figure 15

TROPISMS IN SHOOT GROWTH

growth through bending occurs because the cells elongate more on one side of an organ than on the other. Most changes in direction, particularly in the shoot system, are due to tropisms. Elongation oriented with respect to light intensity is called phototropism and with respect to gravity is called geo-tropism. If the orientation of a lateral is suddenly changed, these tropisms can cause curved growth within a few hours. There is a good deal of disagreement about many aspects of these tropisms, but in both cases the root or shoot appears to have some sort of receptor that can detect the stimulus (light or gravity). The receptor somehow induces lateral transport of auxin so that there is more on one side of the organ than the other. Finally the differential auxin concentration causes dif-ferential cell elongation and ultimately bending.[1] This type of bending occurs only in the zone of cell elongation. Because it is localized, the bend may be quite abrupt.

A third factor, especially important in the orientation of older shoots in the shoot system, is a type of geotropism called reac-tion wood formation. When a stem or branch is tipped out of vertical the pattern of differentiation of cells produced by cam-bial activity changes to form compression wood all along the under side of the leaning branch or stem in conifers and ten-sion wood on the upper side of the lean in angiosperms (our common deciduous hardwood trees). Bending of the stem does not occur for several weeks because it takes that long for reac-tion wood cells to mature. Both types of reaction wood act to bend the stem back toward the vertical. Compression wood expands and tends to push the stem up; tension wood contracts and tends to pull the stem up.[2] The details of reaction wood formation will be considered in the discussion of cambial ac-tivity, but in this section it is important to realize that it is an additional process that is effective in orienting parts of the shoot system. Reaction wood occurs infrequently in the root system and presumably is not significant in orienting roots.

How do these various factors interact to determine branch orientation? Branch orientation is usually described by branch angle. Although the main stem is usually upright, the branches grow at angles to the vertical and to the parent shoot. These angles are characteristic for a species or variety. Spruce often has a relatively large branch angle, maple about 45 degrees and a fastigate variety like lombardy poplar may have a very small angle. There are also the interesting cases of "witches brooms" that develop on some branches of trees where all the laterals grow straight up. In general the angle of higher order branches is greater than the angle of main branches. Short-shoots usually grow out at almost right angles.

The initial direction of elongation of a branch is determined by the angle of the lateral bud on the parent stem, called the angle of insertion. If the bud is pointing at an angle to the stem the branch will originally grow out at that angle because, being attached firmly at the base, they cannot swivel or bend rapidly. This angle of insertion is retained as the angle at the base of branches.

Once freed from the restraints near the base of the branch, the elongating portion of the branch orients according to its preferred angle to the gravitational field. This preferred angle is usually upwards for shoots. Even on horizontal branches the tips of the branches, where elongation has recently occurred, usually point up. This angle of the tip part of the branch is called the geotropic angle. As pointed out above, it takes a certain length of shoot to accomplish the curvature that expresses the geotropic angle. Short-shoots may not have any geotropic angle simply because they are so short. For instance short-shoots in larch that seldom ever reach half an inch in length are essentially uncurved, growing out at the angle of insertion. Short-shoots on red maple, that may grow slowly for 30 years becoming a foot or more long, eventually show a geotropic response so that the tips grow upward even when the branch started out growing down.

There are some exceptions to the generalization that shoots grow vertically. One is that branches of some species of *Araucaria* (a genus of conifers) continue to grow at a specific angle to the vertical even when the branch is removed from the tree and grown separately as a new plant. Some branches appearing to have no geotropic response just hang down, as in weeping willow. Many weeping varieties, however, have a normal geotropic response, but not enough reaction wood is produced to keep the branch upright.

The angle of insertion is at the base of the branch and the geotropic angle is at the elongating tip of the branch, but as the branch grows longer the middle portion usually develops a third, distinct angle. This angle, the angle of inclination, is usually what is meant when talking about the characteristic branch angle of a species. The reason for the development of an angle of inclination is that the branch starts off at an angle to the vertical and as it grows longer it forms laterals and bears an increasingly heavy weight of leaves and branches. This load bends the branch down despite the reaction wood formation in the branch that tends to straighten it back up. The angle of insertion is maintained because the branch is thickest right next to the main stem. The geotropic angle is maintained because the elongating tip continues to grow upwards regardless of the angle of inclination. Gradually the older portion of the branch, originally at the geotropic angle, is bent down by the weight at the tip to the angle of inclination.

Another factor besides weight that keeps branches from growing straight up is the effect of the terminal on branch angle called "epinasty." Epinasty can be thought of as the tendency of the parent branch to force the lateral branch down. Support for the occurrence of epinasty is that when the terminal shoot is

removed the uppermost laterals tend to become upright, presumably because the epinastic forces have been removed and
only the upwards, geotropic force remains. The upwards movement of laterals after injury to the terminal is a common cause
of forking of the main stem of trees. Perhaps the commonest
example is the forking that occurs after insect ("weevil") injury
to white pine leaders where the strongest laterals move up and
become multiple leaders. Another demonstration of the balance
between epinasty and geotropism is the experiment where the
terminal is left intact and the lateral is either tied up or down.
If the lateral is tied up, reaction wood forms to bring the branch
down, presumably due to epinasty. If the branch is tied down
it forms reaction wood to bring the branch back up, presumably
due to geotropism. Sinnott has performed some elegant experiments tying pine branches up, down, in loops, etc. He
claims that in every case compression wood forms so as to return the branch to its original position. Sinnott does not use
epinasty as an explanation of his results, but many of his experiments suggest that the compression induced by imposed
bending may stimulate the reaction wood formation he observed. There has been limited success in replacing the epinastic effect of a leader by applying auxin to the cut surface where
a terminal has been removed. This type of replacement suggests
that epinasty is some sort of variation of apical dominance or
apical control. The only way to sum up epinasty seems to be
that there is clearly some effect on lateral branch angle due to
the presence of the terminal shoot, but it is not clear how this
effect works.[3]

Phototropism is probably not very important in the orientation of most branches in a tree crown. In fact under normal conditions the light is predominantly from above so that it would
be difficult to detect whether upward growth was due to phototropism or to geotropism. However, "apparent phototropism"

is quite common in trees. When a tree is growing under or beside another tree so that part of the crown is heavily shaded, many species will develop a much better crown on the well lit side. It often looks as though the crown had actually moved over toward the light due to phototropism. In most cases what has happened is that the well lit portions of the crown have produced many large, healthy laterals, while the shaded part has produced few laterals that are relatively short-lived. Over the years the crown shifts position, not because the individual branches shift position, but just because new branch production occurs predominantly on one side of the crown.

An interesting example of regulation of shoot orientation by geotropism, phototropism and epinasty is the complicated movements of elongating pine shoots. In spring the terminal and lateral buds elongate and grow straight up. They are strongly geotropic. For a while all the new shoots are growing up and the tree looks as if it were decorated with candles. As these shoots get longer they become phototropic and for a few weeks they go through daily cycles of movement. Every morning the tip of each upright shoot is inclined to the east toward the rising sun and every afternoon toward the west and the setting sun. As elongation slows and stops, this phototropic waving about also stops. When cambial activity begins at the base of the shoots, epinasty begins to have an effect. Only the terminal shoot remains upright while the lateral shoots are finally forced down at angles to the terminal to form the whorl of laterals that is so obvious in pines. In lateral branches even the terminal shoot moves down until it is at about the angle of the rest of the branch. The laterals in turn assume branch angles forming a whorl around the inclined branch leader.

Lateral roots usually grow at about right angles to the parent root, except when new large tips are formed after injury. These new tips tend to grow out at an acute angle and can be called

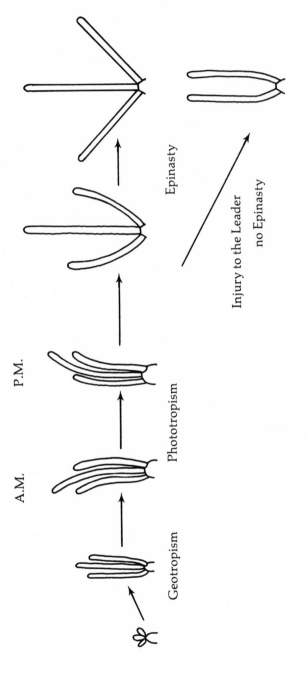

Figure 16

PINE CANDLES

The various phases of tropisms and the elaborate movements of growing pine shoots.

replacement tips because they actually grow in the same direction as the parent tip, they are the same size and do in fact appear to replace the injured parent tip. Although most branch tips tend to grow up, most root tips do *not* tend to grow down. The major woody roots with large tips usually grow horizontally. The small, short roots that grow lateral to the large roots grow at many angles to the vertical and a good many of them actually grow up into the forest floor. Only a very few roots in a root system actually grow down.

Just as in the shoot system, geotropism is very important in determining the orientation of lateral roots once they start elongating. The large lateral root tips that grow horizontally appear to be "plageotropic." This means that if the tip is displaced up it grows down and if it is displaced down it grows up. There must be other factors that regulate the orientation of these roots because they tend to stay at approximately the same depths in the soil even on steep slopes where horizontal growth would bring them to the surface. The lateral roots from these horizontal roots may originally be oriented in any direction depending whether they are on the top, side or bottom of the parent root. There appear to be two possible explanations for the observation that many of these roots grow upwards into the forest floor. Either their geotropic response is to grow upwards, so that the ones that start heading down curve back up, or else these small roots are essentially not geotropic. They may just grow out in whatever direction they started; thus the ones originally oriented upwards grow upwards and proliferate in the forest floor, while those growing downward tend to be less successful unless they happen to encounter a favorable soil environment. It seems that the root system would sample the soil environment more efficiently if the second alternative was true. Then the roots would penetrate all horizons of the soil and proliferate only in the suitable ones.

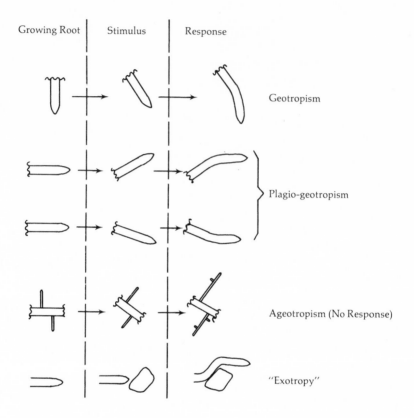

Figure 17

TROPISMS IN ROOT GROWTH

This type of random root growth appears to be the basis of another apparent tropism often called "hydrotropism." Although it may be possible for roots to detect and grow towards higher concentrations of water, in many cases the observation that most of the roots are growing in moist areas is due only to an apparent hydrotropism. The roots start exploiting the whole soil volume, but where the soil gets too dry they die. Those that randomly reach a wet area proliferate and may eventually constitute most of the living root system. The result is that it looks as though the roots had been attracted by the wet area even though no tropism was involved.

Some woody roots do grow down. These are often called "sinkers." They are most common near the trunk of the tree. Even many of the sinkers will grow down for a while but then turn and grow horizontally. It is interesting that although there are relatively few sinkers the overwhelming silvicultural and horticultural emphasis has been on the depth of rooting of trees. Of course depth of rooting is important to tree survival because under drought conditions the upper layers of the soil may become extremely dry. A tree with roots only in the upper layers might not survive drought periods. One question is whether these sinker roots truly grow down because of a geotropic response. If so, are they new roots lateral to horizontal roots or are they horizontal roots that have changed their geotropic response and now grow downwards? McQuilkin in investigating pine roots has suggested that injuries to roots, if they are far enough back of the root tip, cause pre-existing roots that are oriented downwards to become more vigorous and develop into sinkers.[4] Perhaps near the stem where there is adequate nutrition from the stem, small laterals that are growing down may become sufficiently vigorous to form sinkers. It seems unlikely, however, that a root tip would completely change its geotropic response.

A final complicating factor in root orientation is the phenomenon of exotropy. Briefly this means that a root which hits
an obstacle and bends to grow around it tends to bend back to
the original direction when it has gotten by the obstacle. This
type of growth can occur in horizontal roots that grow around
horizontal obstacles, so geotropism is not involved.[5] Exotropy
may complicate the geotropic response when roots grow up or
down around obstacles. Thus, exotropy tends to keep the root
going in a straight line and geotropism tends to maintain the
root in a specific orientation to gravity. Exotropy works even in
a root with no geotropic response. The two phenomena presumably are working all the time as the root tip threads its way
through the soil moving around large and small obstacles.

8

The Process of
Cambial Activity

How the Tree Thickens

 IN THE preceding chapters we have covered lightly the proliferation of the root and shoot system. As mentioned in the introduction, this proliferation requires both strengthening of the stem and an increase in transport capacity between the leaves and the roots. This strengthening occurs in trees by cambial activity. The cambial zone, a thin layer of cells between the bark and the wood of the shoot and root system, contains the meristematic cells, the cambium. From these cells are derived new wood cells, called xylem, that strengthen the central core of the tree and also conduct water and dissolved substances from the roots to the rest of the tree. Derivatives of the cambium also produce new tissue on the inner layer of the bark, the phloem, whose specialized cells conduct sugars and other elaborated materials within the tree. This simple system, xylem to the inside, phloem to the outside, permits trees to attain great size by solving most of the problems that arose from the development of large shoot and root systems as trees evolved.

Tree fanciers who live in temperate zones may not appreciate that cambial activity does not always follow this simple system.[1] Some trees produce a succession of cambia, for instance the mangrove *Avicennia* that lives around the world in tropical and subtropical seashore areas. In this tree the "annual rings" that are so obvious in cross sections of the wood are not formed

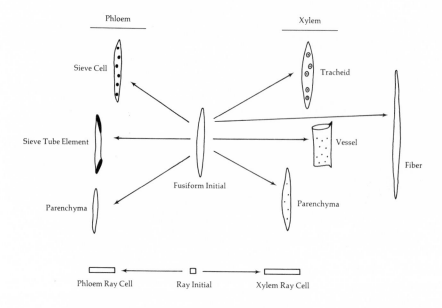

Figure 18

DIFFERENTIATION OF CELL TYPES FROM CAMBIAL INITIALS
*Sieve cells and sieve tube members are specialized for phloem
transport; vessels are specialized for water transport and fibers
for strength; tracheids combine specialization for both strength
and water transport; parenchyma often serve in storage.*

because the wood cells produced every fall are different from those produced in spring. In *Avicennia* the rings are formed because a new cambium has developed and a ring is left quite comparable to those seen in cross sections of garden beets. Just as in beets, these rings are not necessarily annual; there may be 3 or 4 per year in southern Florida. There are many other types of cambial activity, but they will not be considered here. Perhaps the most sensible thing is to proceed with a detailed examination of the simple system of temperate trees, keeping in mind that this system is "normal" only in the temperate zone.

The simplest example of the process of cambial activity is in the conifers, so we will examine cambial activity in conifers in some detail[2] and then discuss the variations that occur in other trees.

Each cambial cell (the cambial initials) produces daughter cells to the inside and outside of the tree, along a radius of a stem cross-section. The initial and its derivatives form a radial file. Thus, all the products of cambial activity—the wood and inner bark—can be subdivided into radial files of cells, each file derived from a common initial cell. Derivatives of the initial cell then pass through the phases of division, enlargement (radial enlargement plus elongation) and differentiation before they finally die. The phase of differentiation in wood cells is primarily occupied with the production of the polysaccharides and lignin that form the secondary wall of each cell. The secondary wall, much like a package containing the living cytoplasm, gives the strength to the wood. After the cytoplasm of the wood cells dies, the cells are left as hollow tubes of cell wall with the insides of the cells interconnected by many pits through the walls that permit water movement from cell to cell. Differentiation in the phloem is somewhat more complex. There are several cell types, cells that are functional in conducting photosynthate and cells that store materials, such as starch,

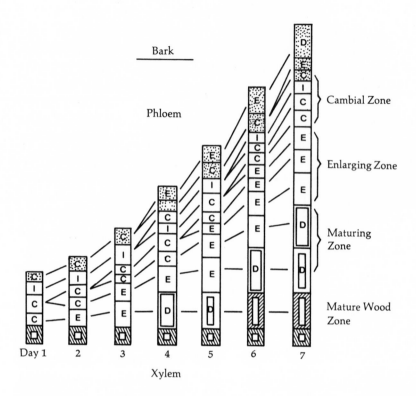

Figure 19

<small>OPERATION OF THE CAMBIUM</small>

*In this pictorial model stippled cells are phloem, cells are lettered
C if in the phase of division (cambial cells), E if in enlargement,
D if in differentiation, and unlabelled if mature.*

crystals or brown colored "tannins." The storage cells stay alive for several years and the sieve cells undergo some dramatic changes, such as loss of the nucleus, but, unlike conducting cells in the wood, are still alive when they are functional.

When the initial cell divides, one daughter cell takes over the function of the initial and the other enters the phase of division. These cells in the phase of division are called mother cells. One tricky part of cambial activity is that the initial cell usually produces xylem mother cells, but sometimes produces phloem mother cells. Thus the same initial cell can produce derivatives to the inside (xylem) or to the outside (phloem) so the radial files are continuous from xylem through the cambial zone to the phloem.

There are actually two types of initial cells, one type is long and thin and called a fusiform ("needle-shaped") initial, the other is almost cubical and is called a ray initial. The fusiform initials produce the vertically elongated cells that, in conifers, constitute about 90% of the wood and phloem. The ray initials produce radially elongated cells in radial files that are called rays. Both types of derivatives pass through comparable phases of division, enlargement and differentiation even though the number of divisions, rates of enlargement and course of differentiation are quite different. Despite the differences, as the cells grow and develop the tissues they form seldom have any air holes between cells (an exception to this is compression wood in conifers that will be discussed later in this chapter). Apparently their growth is regulated by stresses within the developing tissue so that complete cell contacts are maintained.

As the xylem derivatives of the initial enlarge radially they push out the initial cell so that it essentially rides along dividing as it goes and as the derivatives pass through the various phases, zones of division, enlargement and differentiation develop along the radial files. The zone where cells are still dividing is called the cambial zone. Over time the cambial zone moves away from the center of the tree leaving the mature cells behind. Once through the phase of division, cells do not change position relative to each other although during enlargement they may be moved relative to the center of the tree, because of the increasing diameter of the wood. The cambial zone is simply, in a sense, a machine for producing new cells and the machine itself is pushed along by its cellular products.

The simplicity of cambial activity in many conifers, such as hemlock and true fir, is that there is essentially only one fusiform cell type in the wood. All the derivatives pass through the same pathway of differentiation so that the wood is quite a homogeneous material of fusiform tracheids elongated vertically and the radially elongated ray cells. Some conifers like Douglas-fir or bald cypress are a little more complicated. They produce occasional parenchyma cells in the wood instead of all tracheids. The parenchyma are the same shape as tracheids, but they do not develop thick secondary walls. Even more complicated is that many conifers, for instance the pines, develop vertically oriented resin ducts in the wood. These resin ducts start in the xylem mother cells. In cross section a small group of cells develops that has denser contents than the other mother cells; they later split apart forming the duct in the center and a lining of parenchymatous epithelial cells. There may be a series of resin ducts formed at the same time around the stem, separated by "normal" tracheids. So in this case certain cells in certain files receive a different signal to become resin canals. Another aspect of resin canals is that they are formed by a number of different cells up and down the tree, but these cells are in vertical strands so that the canal is continuous up and down the tree. There must be some vertical regulation to ensure that the canals are continuous.

The complexities of the conifers seem insignificant when compared to the complexities of angiosperm wood, because angiosperm wood normally has at least three types of wood cells. These differences all arise during enlargement and differentiation. There are still only ray initials and one type of fusiform initial in angiosperms and the whole process of cell production by cell division is essentially the same as in conifers. The differences arise during enlargement when some of the derived cells enlarge radially only a little, although they may elongate a great deal, then form thick secondary walls. These cells are the fibers that are specialized to give strength to the wood. Other cells enlarge just a little bit and do not form thick walls, developing into parenchyma cells, apparently specialized for storage. Some cells enlarge a great deal radially, do not elongate, but form thick walls except on the ends where one or more relatively large holes develop as the cell dies. These barrel-like cells are the vessel elements that are specialized for water conduction. Just as in the resin canals, there is some vertically oriented regulation that results in the vessel elements aligning to form long vertical tubes called vessels. Water moves straight through these tubes with minimum resistance.

These different types of wood cells do not develop randomly. There is a consistent pattern of cell types that is the basis of wood anatomy.[3] Each tree species produces wood with such a consistent pattern that it can be identified and distinguished from other species. There are two basic types of wood in the hardwoods (angiosperms). In one type the vessels are all about the same size and are scattered fairly evenly through the wood. This type, called "diffuse porous," is found in maples, birches, beeches, and cherries. In the other type, extremely large vessels, often visible to the naked eye, are formed at the beginning of each growth ring and the vessels formed through the rest of the growth ring are only one-tenth the diameter of the first vessels. This type, called "ring porous," is found in oaks, ashes, elms, and hickories.

The development of these patterns of cell types seems to be based on the distribution of vessels. Analysis of the structure of mature wood suggests that there is not only a vertically oriented regulation that determines the alignment of one vessel element with the next, but also radial and tangential regulations that maintain a consistent pattern in cross section. In different woods there appear to be two types of factors regulating distribution in cross section. One factor determines whether vessels occur singly or in groups. If they do occur in groups this suggests an "epidemic" distribution as though the presence of one vessel stimulated the development of another adjacent vessel. Even in woods where vessels occur in groups the groups are separated and here a type of regulation based on exclusion seems to operate so that a group of vessels excludes the development of other vessels for some distance around it. In the first case the assumption is that the vessel produces something that stimulates further vessel development and in the second case the assumption is that the vessels either produce something that inhibits vessel development or else use up something that is required.

The distribution of vessels then appears to regulate the distribution of other cell types. Parenchyma are usually distributed in some relation to the vessels, often surrounding them. Fibers essentially fill in what is left. Ray cells are basically the same in hardwoods as in conifers, but in hardwoods are aggregated into rays that are much larger and more complex.

The observation that vessels are interwoven into a three-dimensional network further complicates development of the vessel pattern.[4] First of all, the vessels are not just parallel tubes in the wood. They are tubes that interconnect and sometimes

end at junctions with other tubes. Second, this whole complicated vessel pattern must be initiated right at the edge of the
cambial zone because vessels immediately start to enlarge faster
than adjacent cells. Thus, when the pattern is blocked out the
radial distances are much compressed compared to those sep-
arating mature vessels. Once the vessels start enlarging they
get so big that they occupy the space of several radial files and
cell production in adjacent files has to stop temporarily.

So far we have just considered the development of individual
radial files, but a little consideration of what happens as these
files get longer and the tree increases in diameter shows that
the cambium must make adjustments to the increase in circumference. The first adjustment is that the cambium must produce
new radial files to keep the wood from developing radial splits
as the circumference increases. In the 1920's I. W. Bailey's
classic work on cambial activity demonstrated that the cambium
primarily produces new files rather than having the initials enlarge tangentially.[5] The cambium also has to produce new ray
initials to make new rays. M. W. Bannan, in a series of pains-
taking investigations,[6] has shown that fusiform initials require
a certain number of contacts with ray cells, presumably because
nourishment moves radially into the cambium from the phloem
through the rays. Bannan showed that fusiform initials without
enough ray contacts did not survive. Therefore, the cambium
must not only produce new files of fusiform cells, but it must
also produce new files of ray cells to permit survival of the fusiform cells.

Largely through the work of Bailey and Bannan the process
by which the cambium produces new files of fusiform and ray
cells is now quite well worked out for conifers, and other investigators seem to be finding that the same general principles
apply to the cambium of angiosperms. Basically, the fusiform
initial, which predominantly divides in a plane parallel to the

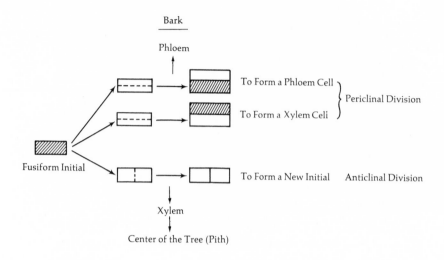

Figure 20

TYPES OF DIVISION OF A FUSIFORM INITIAL

surface of the bark producing a mother cell and an initial cell in the radial file, occasionally divides in a plane perpendicular to the bark producing two initial cells. Ultimately these two initial cells will produce two radial files for a net gain of one radial file. In storied cambia like black locust the perpendicular division divides the cell completely lengthwise so that the two daughter initial cells are the same length. In most cases the new wall is S-shaped and the two daughter initial cells are somewhat longer than half the length of the parent initial but shorter than the full length. These shorter initials gradually elongate back to about the original length of the parent when they redivide perpendicularly. Bannan has estimated that it takes about 3–4 years for the initials to elongate between perpendicular divisions in arborvitae (*Thuja occidentalis*). During its elongation the initial cell continues to undergo parallel divisions. As a result the derivatives gradually get longer as the initial elongates because parallel divisions are almost always the full length of the initial cell.

This type of perpendicular division produces the needed extra radial files. Elongation of the new initial cells maintains, and even increases, the average length of the derivatives. But where do the new ray initials come from? The answer is that they come from unequal perpendicular divisions where the small cell becomes a ray initial and the large cell stays a fusiform initial. There are several types of these unequal divisions; a small cell may be cut out of the side of a fusiform cell, or off the tip, or a medium sized cell may be subdivided by successive divisions into a series of ray initials.[7] Bannan has also found that some fusiform initials that are small and lack ray contacts may even be lost from the cambium.

An interesting aspect of these perpendicular divisions is that there seems to be some sort of feedback type of control over the fate of new initial cells. Apparently each fusiform initial must be in contact with several rays to survive. If, after a perpendicular division, one of the daughter initials is too small to have enough ray contacts then it is highly probable that it will subdivide to develop a new ray. Thus, rays develop in the very areas where there are not enough of them.

Both conifers and angiosperms produce wood that appears to be specialized for bending up leaning stems. This wood is called reaction wood, because it is often assumed to be formed solely as a reaction to the tipping of a stem or any branch that is not vertical. Reaction wood in conifers is called compression wood.[8] It forms on the under side (the compressed side) of tilted stems and branches. The mature wood is actually under compression; it is trying to enlarge, so it tends to right the organ by pushing it up. Compression wood is easily seen in most species because it is a dark red-brown color, rather like the latewood in annual rings. Under the microscope compression wood cells are round in outline with spaces between the cells, instead of the usual closely packed hexagons of "normal" wood. The walls are much thicker than usual. They are highly ligni- fied, and special microscope techniques show that the cellulose microfibrils of the secondary wall are oriented at an unusually large angle to the long axis of the cells. These differences in the cell wall are presumably related to the great longitudinal, ex- pansive force that the cells develop. One recent suggestion for the origin of the force is that during lignification of the cell wall as the lignin is deposited on the cellulose framework the lignin swells between the cellulose microfibrils, forcing them apart and lengthening the cell.[9]

Reaction wood in angiosperms is called tension wood. It forms on the upper side of leaning stems or branches (the ten- sion side). Tension wood is actually in tension, trying to shrink, and tends to pull the stem or branch upright. It does the same job as compression wood but on the opposite side of leaning stems and with the opposite stress. Tension wood is not usually obvious except under the microscope. In sections it can be readily seen because the fibers are almost unlignified and be- cause there are so few vessels. The fibers have an extra layer of secondary wall, and the microfibrils of this layer are almost parallel to the long axis of the cells, just the opposite of compres- sion wood cells. Recent investigations suggest that the tension in the wood develops partially due to swelling between the microfibrils that tends to shorten the fibers (but there is very little lignin to account for this swelling). There are a number of observations using the electron microscope that show that the extra layer of secondary wall swells out during differentiation and presses against the external layers of the wall. This type of pressure from inside could also lead to the development of a tensile stress as the cell shortened.

9

Regulation of Cambial Activity

The Timing, Rate, and Type of Thickening

THE THREE PHASES of cambial activity, division, enlargement and differentiation, each have separate sets of controls. Division restricts the whole process of cambial activity because if no cells are produced then the other phases cannot take place. But given that cells are produced, there are all possible combinations from large cells with thin walls and small cells with thick walls (the normal pattern in annual rings) to large cells with thick walls and small cells with thin walls. Under certain environmental or experimental conditions it seems that each phase may vary in intensity independent of the other phases. All the phases of cambial activity are modified by environmental conditions such as temperature or moisture, but specific regulation seems to be through the leaves, directly or indirectly. In fact, most of the variation in cambial activity is a response to photosynthate or growth regulators (auxin, gibberellin, inhibitor) produced by the leaves.

Each spring cambial divisions must be initiated after the winter rest period. In conifers and diffuse porous trees, cambial activity starts just below the buds as they become active and then activity spreads gradually down the tree. Removal of the buds stops initiation, but the effect of the buds can be partially replaced by auxin. The inference is that auxin produced by the buds moves down the stem and initiates cambial activity so that the spread of initiation down the stem is determined by the movement of the auxin. In ring porous trees, cambial activity starts before the buds become active, beginning over all of the

tree at about the same time. The first large vessels are formed
before the leaves grow out. Wareing has shown that in ring
porous trees there is a great deal of auxin precursor present in
the dormant cambial zone and that this precursor appears to
be rapidly converted to auxin simultaneously over the whole
tree.[1] Auxin apparently is still necessary to initiate cambial
activity, but in ring porous trees it does not have to come
directly from the expanding buds and leaves where it is produced.

Once divisions are started, cell production by the cambial
zone is a function of both the rate of redivision of cells in the
dividing phase and the number of cells in that phase. In other
words the rate of cell production is the same (2/day, for example) whether there are 10 cells that divide every 5 days or
20 cells that divide every 10 days. A good indication of the rate
of division is the percentage of the cells in the phase of division
that are actually dividing. The faster the rate of division, the
higher the percentage of cells that are dividing. This percentage
of dividing cells is called the mitotic index (mitosis being the
division of the cell nucleus). The number of cells in the cambial
zone, the cells that can divide, is lowest in dormant trees and
greatest during the period of weeks, or even months, shortly
after activity is initiated in the spring. The mitotic index is
greatest when cell number is greatest. During this period of
maximum cambial zone cells in conifers, the mitotic index of
fast and slow growing trees of a species on one area is about the
same. The differences in the rate of cell production between
trees are due almost entirely to differences in the number of
cells that are dividing.[2] Apparently the rate of division is
pretty much genetically determined, but the length of time that
cells remain in the phase of division can be regulated by the
activity of the crown. The regulation may be through the
amount of available photosynthate or the amount of growth

regulators produced by the leaves. Both of these would be greater in dominant trees and less in suppressed trees and so far there are no data to separate the two possible regulatory mechanisms.

As the summer progresses cell production slows and stops. Mitotic activity drops to zero and the number of cells in the cambial zone returns to the minimum number present in the dormant tree. Apparently cell production continues as long as the leaves are still producing auxin. In diffuse porous trees only enlarging leaves produce auxin; mature leaves do not, so that when late leaf production and leaf growth stop around the middle of July, cambial activity also stops because there is no more auxin moving down from the stem. In conifers and ring porous hardwoods the mature leaves continue to produce auxin and cambial activity can continue long after leaf growth has stopped.[3] In pines some cell production may continue even after the first frost of the autumn.

An additional factor that seems to affect the rate of cell production is the effect of wind sway. The tree stem sways in the wind and as it bends the cambial zone is subjected to repeated strains (changes in length) and stresses (changes in forces acting). This sway appears to stimulate cell production. Trees that sway in only one direction tend to become oval because they produce more wood in the direction parallel to the sway than perpendicular. Trees that are guyed so that the stem cannot sway have an overall reduction in cell production in the lower stem. Somehow the stresses and strains induced by swaying stimulate cell production. Stresses and strains in themselves probably do not affect the process, but they might affect the redistribution of auxin moving down the stem or sensitize the cells so that they are more responsive to the auxin that is present. The phenomenon itself is well established but the mechanism of the phenomenon is not.[4]

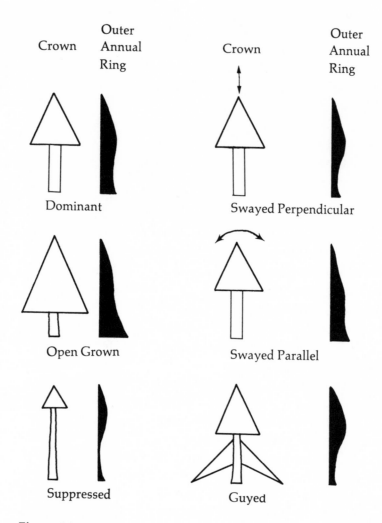

Figure 21

LONGITUDINAL DISTRIBUTION OF CAMBIAL ACTIVITY
The relation of crown size (left) and sway (right) to the distribution of cambial activity in the outermost annual ring.

Final cell diameters go through regular annual cycles. The largest cells are produced during the spring and summer and constitute the early wood of the annual ring. Towards the end of periods of cambial activity, cells enlarge less and the late wood of the annual ring contains relatively small diameter cells. The diameter of the cells seems to be proportional to the auxin concentration and inversely proportional to water stress. The width is greatest during stem and needle elongation. In some species like red pine the diameter begins to decrease slowly after shoot elongation stops but needle elongation is still active and then drops rapidly as needle elongation stops. In other species like white pine there is no drop in diameter marking the end of shoot elongation. Larson has successfully regulated tracheid diameter by regulating the photoperiod, because needle elongation is regulated by photoperiod, and also by the addition of external auxin. In experiments where auxin is added to stems, cell diameter increases as auxin increases, up to a maximum diameter, but if the stem is treated to reduce the amount of internal auxin reaching the cambium (by adding triiodobenzoic acid to block polarized auxin transport), then the diameters decrease.

Somewhat the same results have been found for vessel size in hardwoods. Fiber diameter scarcely changes throughout annual rings, although there is a sudden decrease in the last few cells. Vessels, however, are larger in the early wood and smaller in the late wood. The huge vessels of ring porous trees are somewhat special. They develop very early, before the leaves, presumably under conditions of high auxin, but in any case under completely different conditions from any cells in conifers or diffuse porous trees. Cambial activity can be induced in dormant hardwood stem segments by adding growth regulators and the diameter of the vessels formed is proportional to the concentration of auxin supplied. Vessel diameter

"Normal" Latewood

Drought Latewood

"Normal" Earlywood

"Long Day" Latewood

Figure 22

TRACHEIDS

*The range of combinations of
radial diameters and wall thickness
observable in tracheids.*

is reduced if the segments are grown under conditions of water stress.

Experiments applying growth regulators mixed in lanolin to the tip end of stem segments shed some light on other problems of cambial activity. One such problem is why some cells become vessels and others not. In stem segments either gibberellin alone, or auxin alone, initiates cambial activity. With gibberellin alone there is no production of vessels, while with auxin alone vessels develop, but only a few cells are produced. Apparently there must be auxin moving down the stem, normally from the leaves, to permit any vessel development. Presumably at the levels of auxin normally occurring in stems the number of cells that become vessels is limited; perhaps they use up all the auxin or perhaps they somehow inhibit other cells, but the auxin is necessary to permit the extraordinary radial enlargement associated with vessel development.[5]

Another basic question in the study of cambial activity is why most daughter cells resulting from divisions of initial cells become xylem mother cells, but some become phloem mother cells. Some experiments suggest that the ratio of xylem to phloem in stem segments can be regulated by varying the ratio of auxin to gibberellin. High auxin produced relatively more xylem and high gibberellin produced relatively more phloem. These data certainly do not solve the problem of the determination of daughter cells after the division of the initial, but they do suggest that the determination is somehow, like most other aspects of cambial activity, regulated by the growth regulators coming from the leaves.

The aspect of differentiation that has been studied most in the development of the xylem is secondary wall formation. Secondary wall thickness also follows a pattern across an annual ring, just as radial diameter does. Usually annual rings of conifers have early wood cells that are large in diameter and thin-walled, and latewood cells that are small in diameter and thick-walled. The characteristic dense, dark latewood is the result of these narrow, thick-walled cells. In white pine, which has relatively little latewood, the thick-walled cells are formed only after needle elongation has stopped so the increase in thickness coincides with the rapid decrease in diameter as cambial activity stops. In red pine, there is usually a good deal of latewood because thick walls begin to develop after shoot elongation stops, but before needle elongation stops, so there is a zone of relatively large diameter, thick-walled cells and then the annual ring is terminated by small diameter, thick-walled cells.

Young red pine, grown under continuous long days at high light intensity, continue to produce large-celled early wood, but the cell walls get thicker and thicker until they produce what is called "long day latewood." On the other hand, under drought conditions pines may produce lots of narrow cells with thin walls. Thus, although thick walls are usually associated with narrow cells, all different combinations may occur.[6]

There are basically two theories about the regulation of cell wall thickness. One is that the thickness is related to the photosynthate left after respiration and growth of other parts of the tree. Thus, normal thick-walled latewood is formed after the drain on photosynthate by needle and shoot elongation has stopped. There is a positive relationship between light intensity and wall thickness, presumably because as light increases photosynthesis increases. There is also a negative relationship between the night temperature, which increases night respiration, and wall thickness. High temperature reduced wall thickness by reducing net photosynthesis. Larson's experiments with radioactive carbon dioxide also suggest that wall thickness is related to net photosynthesis as above.[7]

The other theory is that wall thickness is regulated by the length of time that cells are in the phase of cell wall thickening. Earlywood cells differentiate so fast that cell walls are thin, but latewood cells stay near the phloem for a long time and wall thickening proceeds for a long time. In larch, short days cause the production of an inhibitor that permits walls to be synthesized for a longer period, perhaps by retarding the breakdown of the cytoplasm.[8]

It seems quite likely that both these theories are correct and that they should somehow be combined. For instance conditions of high net photosynthesis might increase the rate of wall thickening, whereas an inhibitor could increase the length of time for thickening. Both would result in a thicker wall. At least, the two theories do not seem mutually exclusive.

One aspect of the regulation of cambial activity that is important to the tree is the production of reaction wood. When a stem is leaning the course of differentiation of cambial derivatives changes. In jack pine the developing tracheid must be leaning throughout the whole phase of enlargement and differentiation to become a typical compression wood cell. Just tilting a seedling during the enlargement phase did not affect the cell wall thickening phase.

For years there has been an argument about whether compression wood is formed due to the effect of gravity or to the effect of the compressive stress on the under side of the leaning stem (*vice versa* for angiosperms). Jaccard's experiment of bending stems into circles showed that compression wood always formed on the under side of the stem whether the wood was on the inside of the circle (in compression) or on the outside (in tension).

The hypothesis that developed was that in leaning stems auxin was transported laterally and was at a high concentration on the underside. The circle of proof was completed when it was shown that high auxin concentrations on upright conifer stems could induce compression wood and low auxin concentrations (induced by TIBA blockage of auxin transport) on upright angiosperm stems induced tension wood formation. Thus, it seems that the same mechanism of lateral auxin transport and accumulation on the underside of the stem can account for both compression and tension wood formation because the former develops in high concentrations and the latter in low concentrations.

There are, unfortunately, many examples where reaction wood does not form on the "normal" upper side of leaning

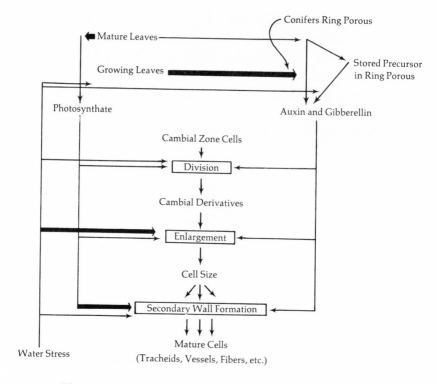

Figure 23

REGULATION OF CAMBIAL ACTIVITY

Shown in a flow chart.

stems or branches. Perhaps the best known is in branch epinasty. If a branch normally forms reaction wood on one side, when it is bent up, lessening the branch angle, it may form reaction wood on the opposite side and this reaction wood tends to return the branch to its original position. There are other experiments where branches are disoriented and they form compression wood on the tops, bottoms, sides or even spiraling along the branch.[9]

It is difficult to see how epinasty could affect lateral transport. It is even more difficult to see how transport is affected in the more sophisticated bending experiments. These experiments seem to suggest that perhaps stress does somehow enter the picture of regulating compression wood formation, perhaps in collusion with gravity. In complex bends about the only consistent stimulus-response relationship seems to be between stress and compression wood. Perhaps stress, or rather strain (changes in length resulting from applied stress), can affect auxin distribution, but the answer is not known yet.

10
Distribution Problems
Where does Thickening Occur?

 WE HAVE ANALYZED a tree part by part, a common method for breaking down large, or complex, systems. To make the story complete, however, we must put the tree back together again. We shall analyze two examples of how the tree operates as a unit. Both these examples revolve about the same problem, the distribution of the photosynthate produced by the leaves. All growth uses this photosynthate as energy source and as building material for biosynthetic processes. Thus, photosynthate from the leaves must ultimately supply the growing roots that are often more than a hundred feet away from the leaves. The anchoring portion of the root system must be made stronger as must the supporting stem. The branching system must increase. As already mentioned, branch elongation is largely based on photosynthate that has been stored from a previous year. The branches must also be strengthened to bear their increasing load of leaves. The input to this system called "tree" is the energy from sunlight; photosynthesis converts this light energy to chemical energy in a multitude of forms that we lump together here and call photosynthate. The tree has evolved efficient mechanisms for distributing this photosynthate to the various growing organs, the vast cambial surface, and storage areas, so that the tree will become the tallest plant. Just growing tall to get leaves in the sun is not enough to ensure success if the rest of the plant, the supporting cast of the roots, stem and branching system, does

not grow apace to keep the relatively delicate balance between parts required to maintain a whole plant.

The first example of the tree as an intact system is seen in the regulation of stem form. The stem must be strong enough to support the crown under the wide range of stresses that a tree undergoes as it passes through hurricanes, ice storms, etc. There are plenty of examples of trees that are broken or uprooted by unusually severe storms. But it is not in the best interests of the tree to be designed for excessive stem strength, because a tree that diverts too much photosynthate to strengthening the stem may be robbing the crown or root system of materials needed for its expansion so that the tree can not grow tall enough fast enough to compete with other trees.

There are several requirements for the distribution system that regulates stem form by regulating the distribution of cambial activity. Wood must be produced so that the stem, as a load bearing beam in the engineering sense, is efficiently designed to withstand the stresses that develop by the swaying crown. Thickening the stem increases its strength rapidly because stiffness is related to the fourth power of the diameter. The anchoring roots must be strong enough to keep the tree from pulling out of the ground. The water transport capacity of the wood must also be maintained. This last requirement is usually no problem because wood contains both cells for strength and cells for transport so a system that is designed for strength will have adequate transport capacity if the initial mix of transporting cells is adequate. By considering only upright stems we do not have to worry about production of reaction wood that has a lower transport capacity than normal wood.[1]

Just what is the product of this distribution system? Ultimately of course it is the external shape of the stem, but this shape is built up by a series of annual sheaths of wood, which in cross section show up as annual rings. In terms of stem form it is more useful to consider a longitudinal section of the annual sheath, because you can picture how the sheaths are added together making a laminated structure. The longitudinal pattern of wood thickness from top to bottom of a tree can be related to the general vigor of the crown. The average, forest grown tree that is not overcrowded has the following longitudinal pattern: the width of the annual sheath is small at the top of the tree; increases in width down the tree to a point that just about coincides with the largest, most productive portion of the crown; going down the stem below the crown the width remains constant; near the base of the stem it increases; within 2 meters, or less, out along the roots there is very little cambial activity, there are usually even many incomplete sheaths of wood (discontinuous rings in cross section) in the further portions of woody roots.[2]

In an open grown tree with a well developed crown, the pattern is basically the same within the crown, but different below the crown. The width of the sheath increases slowly below the crown where the forest-grown tree had a fairly constant width. Again, there is an increase in width at the butt swell and the zone of rapid taper in the roots.

In a suppressed tree with a small crown that makes very little photosynthate the pattern is also basically the same within the crown, although the widths are all less than in more vigorous trees. Below the crown, sheath width decreases and in extremely suppressed trees there may be no growth at all along the middle portion of the trunk. There usually is still some butt swell at the base of the stem.

Thus, the general pattern is that the width of the annual sheath increases from the top of the tree to the most productive area of the crown. Below this point—essentially along the main stem—width may increase in vigorous trees, remain about constant in less vigorous trees or even decrease in suppressed non-vigorous trees. At the base of the stem there is an increase at the butt swell and this increase goes out the roots a short distance before the sheath is greatly reduced in width in the further portions of the root system.

There are a number of factors that enter into the determination of the distribution of cambial activity over this sheath. A major factor, perhaps the most important one, is that all the materials necessary for cambial activity come ultimately from the crown, although possibly indirectly through stored materials. Experiments in which the phloem is girdled to stop the movement of materials down the stem to the cambium show that cell division and enlargement are dependent on materials currently moving down the stem. They are essentially unable to mobilize stored materials below a girdle. Presumably the most important short term requirement is for the growth substances produced by the leaves. They are required for initiation of activity and, after movement is stopped by girdling, activity ceases within two weeks below the girdle. Photosynthate is, however, required for activity and it must all move down the phloem from the leaves. Just based on these facts one might predict that most of the growth would occur near the source of supply. In fact, the increase in sheath width going down the crown does seem to reflect the increasing supply of photosynthate and regulators. In very suppressed trees that grow only within the crown the distribution of activity again seems related to proximity to the source and there may be no activity at all much below the crown of a severely suppressed tree.

Distribution within the crown is not due solely to proximity to the source of photosynthate. Disbudding experiments on pine trees suggest that growing shoots somehow keep cambial activity in the upper stem. Completely disbudded pine trees may have just as much cambial activity as normal trees, because the old needles produce photosynthate, but none of it is used in shoot elongation. This activity is, however, displaced down the stem much in the manner that sway, discussed below, displaces activity.[3]

Below the crown the distribution of activity does not evenly decrease with distance from the source, except in the suppressed trees. Here the factor of sway enters the picture. There are a number of guying experiments that show that a guyed tree (usually guyed just below the crown) grows less along the stem and at the butt swell than a tree that is free to sway in the wind. In addition, the growth above the guy point, both cambial activity and elongation, is greater in the guyed tree than in the free tree. Thus, a major factor in determining the distribution of cambial activity below the crown and in the anchoring portion of the root system is the effect of wind sway. The general effect is that sway causes redistribution of activity from the upper to the lower portion of the stem.

Larson has performed some experiments that nicely summarize these distribution problems. His experiments combined pruning the crown, to reduce the input of photosynthate and regulators, and comparing guyed and swaying trees. He found that reducing the amount of photosynthate and regulators by pruning caused a shifting upwards of the distribution of activity just as in suppressed trees, but that activity could be shifted downwards by swaying the trees.[4] The basic distribution seems to be related to distance from the source, but it is modified by sway. A third factor appears to be the operation of the various sinks represented by the lower part of the stem, the root system, etc. These parts of the tree are a long way from the source, they are not modified by sway, but they do grow and they do get materials from the crown.

A simple model to represent this distribution system would be a water distribution system of a long main pipe, the phloem, through which the photosynthate moves. All along this pipe are the users of photosynthate, developing leaves, elongating shoots, cambial activity in branches, stem and roots, and elongating roots. All these users require a certain minimum amount of photosynthate to survive, the amounts used in respiration, annual production of organs, and other vital processes. If these requirements are not met, the whole tree dies because it is dependent on all its parts. If there is more than this minimal amount of photosynthate, then each user uses more and some photosynthate will ultimately go into storage. This system is reminiscent of the relationship between supply and elastic demand in economic theory. All the photosynthate is used up somewhere, but the question is where. The whole distribution system of a healthy tree is beautifully in balance so that the stem is strong enough, the root system big enough and storage large enough to produce the biggest, tallest crown with the largest leaf area so that the total amount of photosynthate will be maximized.

Use of photosynthate along the stem is determined partly by proximity to the supply. Farther away the magnitude of use, perhaps analogous to the relative size of the drain pipe hooked up to the main pipe of the phloem, is determined partly by the size of the user, for instance the amount of meristematic tissue, and partly by the rate of activity of the meristem. This rate can be modified by sway, in the case of the cambium. Judging from the swaying experiments, if use is cut down in one area, for instance by guying, then it increases in another, in this case the crown. Presumably the amount used is also partly regulated by the amount available—sort of a Parkinson's law for photosynthate use.

One of the things that happens after thinning a forest stand is that the distribution of cambial activity is shifted down the tree. This could happen for one or both of two reasons. The crowns of the trees receive more light, produce more photosynthate, and thus the stimulating effect of nearness to the supply can extend farther down the tree. The other factor is that thinning allows increased sway of the residual stems and probably increases the amount of wind in the stand. Under natural conditions it is always hard to separate the effect of photosynthate production and sway on distribution of cambial activity because the very conditions that produce high photosynthate, open grown trees, also produce the most sway.

Another example of the distribution of photosynthate, really a sort of sub-example of the general problem of distribution of cambial activity, is the regulation of the angle of inclination in conifer branches. The angle of inclination of conifer branches usually is greater in the lower branches of the crown, but the more vigorous the branch is the less the angle of inclination. Thus, branches that are severely shaded have large branch angles but some branches, like those formed after weevil damage in pines, are extremely vigorous, upright and may be equal to the main stem.[5]

What regulates the angle? As previously mentioned, the angle is the result of the weight of the branch and its needles pushing down and the strength of the branch itself resisting that push. There is also the existence of some epinastic force downwards due to the presence of active growth above the branch. Conifer branches can produce compression wood that is stronger than regular wood and can also actually develop a positive force to move the branch. Again the amount of movement in response to compression wood formation will depend on the strength of the branch.

As a branch grows it gets longer, and it produces more needles. So both the load on the branch base and the amount of photosynthate produced increase. Part of this photosynthate is used in the cambial activity of the branch that maintains branch angle, most of it is used for growth of the rest of the tree. Indeed if a branch is not producing extra photosynthate for the rest of the tree it usually dies. Thus, the maintenance of branch angle is a function of the proportion of photosynthate from the branch that is diverted to branch strengthening. The stem appears to have a much higher priority than the branches, so unless the branch is extremely vigorous it does not stay strong enough to support its own weight.

Another physical source of downwards force on the branch is the wedging action of the wood added above the branch, in the branch angle. As both the stem and the branch increase in diameter the angle of insertion is gradually filled in and the branch base is incorporated into the stem forming knots. The wood in the angle is in compression, often distorted, so it tends to push the branch down. This wedging action may be a factor in the "epinastic" effect of active growth above a lateral branch.

The branch bends near the base because the load is greatest there, but right at the base the branch is strongest because of of the buttressing effect of the growth of the stem combining with branch growth. Much of the wood in the buttress is compression wood. There is also compression wood on the vertical stem just below the branch, and on the underside along the branch. The importance of this compression wood is, first, that it has a positive righting effect, pushing up on the branch, due to its tendency to elongate during differentiation. Second, compression wood is denser and requires more photosynthate than normal wood. Thus, the greater the angle of the branch, the more material is available for use of the rest of the tree if branch angle is maintained.

The regulation of branch angle clearly shows that compression wood is not formed solely from the effect of gravity. Bending branches upwards often can cause compression wood to form on the upper side of the branch. In some southern pines compression wood may form in alternating arcs, first a strong one underneath the branch and then a weak one on top, as though the underneath compression wood had bent the branch up and then the upper compression wood had reacted to bend it back down. Under normal conditions compression wood also forms on the upright portion of the stem under the branch, that forms the branch buttress. These various observations seem to be explained by a single hypothesis. It seems established that compression wood forms under conditions of high auxin. The problem is how those conditions are created. One factor is gravity, which apparently redistributes auxin so the concentration is greater on the lower side of the branch. Another factor could be stress or the strain induced by stress. This factor appears to modify the gravity induced redistribution so that the high auxin is in the concave portion of a bent branch. In a permanently bent and restrained branch the new wood formed in the bend of a branch will soon relieve the stress, the branch will be permanently bent, and then gravity redistribution will predominate as before. In cases where the convex side is also the lower side, then the effects of gravity and stress are additive and difficult to separate. There appear to be two possible mechanisms for the action of stress. Either stress (or strain) actually causes redistribution of auxin, or it somehow sensitizes cambial activity so that it reacts as though the auxin concentration had been increased. Whatever the mechanism, the effect appears to be that if the stress is applied for more than a few weeks, then compression wood is formed because the cells pass through all phases of development under high auxin. If the stress is only short term, as in tree sway, then compression wood does not form because the cells are not constantly under high auxin conditions, but the amount of cells produced does increase to modify stem form in response to the distribution of the stresses and strains induced by sway.

Growth of the Whole Tree

Three Kinds of Interaction Among the Parts of a Tree

 To A LARGE EXTENT during this book the tree has been treated separately by components— the branches, roots, and the cambium. In this last chapter I would like to emphasize how these various components interact to produce the characteristic growth of the tree as a whole system. These interactions can be distinguished into three types: nutritive, correlative, and competitive. These classes of interaction are not independent of each other, for instance nutritive interactions may modify the response to correlative interactions; in other words, there are even interactions among the interactions, just to complicate the matter further. Correlative and competitive interactions are the most important ones for this book because they are the ones that are the major determinants of form, and form is the major attribute that distinguishes trees from other plants.

Nutritive interaction can be understood by knowing that all tissues require photosynthate, water and minerals in relatively large amounts for growth. Leaves produce the photosynthate, roots take up the water and minerals. Thus, the leaves get water and minerals from the roots, the roots get photosynthate from the leaves, the cambium must import all its required growth factors from another part of the plant. One might predict that the various organs could grow independently if supplied with required external factors and this is the basis of organ culture. Roots, shoots and cambial tissue can all be grown independent of the rest of the plant in test tubes if the growth factors of the

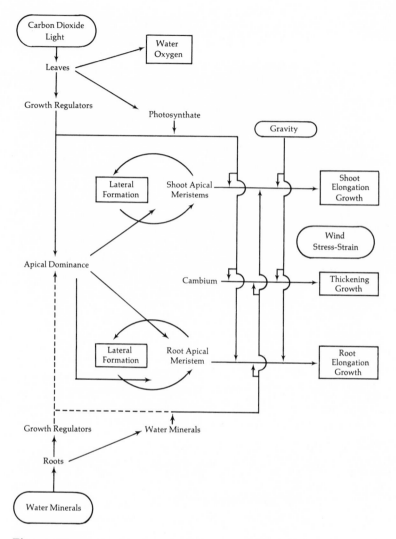

Figure 24

TREE GROWTH

A flow chart that tries to tie together the subject covered in this book. Items in circles are inputs from the environment those in boxes are output either to the environment or as additions to the tree in tree growth. The dotted lines from root-produced growth regulators are because their role is not known. The lines from apical dominance cross lines from lateral formation where inhibition of the process occurs.

particular missing organ are supplied to it. There are many other growth factors besides photosynthate, water and minerals that may be required in minute amounts for organ growth. Roots require vitamins produced by the shoot, cambium requires growth regulators and for normal activity it requires radially applied pressure. Most organs, however, can be grown in relatively simple, defined media when they are isolated from the rest of the plant.[1]

Correlative relationships arise when one organ produces regulators which are transported to another organ where they modify growth. As pointed out above, the general nutritional status of the plant or organ may modify the growth response to these correlative interactions. One example of correlative relationships is the apical dominance and apical control that appears to occur in both the root and shoot system. These processes have been discussed in detail already, but essentially growth regulators moving from other organs can determine whether new lateral organs are produced and how they develop. This occurs in the classical example of apical inhibition of lateral bud growth and also appears to occur in the inhibition of late-leaf development on lateral short-shoots. In the roots apical dominance appears to regulate the size of lateral root primordia. Apical control regulates the angle of lateral organs to the parent organ and the relative growth of the lateral. Both dominance and control appear to be stronger in plants of poor nutritional status. Most work on dominance has stressed the role of auxins produced by the shoot tips and expanding leaves. There is increasing evidence that roots can exert correlative regulation through the production of gibberellins and cytokinins.

Almost all aspects of cambial activity are subject to correlative modification. Activity requires auxin from the leaves and normal differentiation requires an external supply of gibberellin.

Stress-strain and gravity appear to modify the distribution of regulators in modifying cambial activity. Stress-strain is almost correlative, and indeed is a nice example of feedback interaction. The stress-strain comes partially from the weight and mostly from swaying due to the sail effect of the crown. Cambial activity is stimulated and the stem is strengthened where stress-strain is greatest. This strengthening reduces the sway and thus reduces the stress-strain stimulus. Gravity effects are not strictly correlative, but the role of gravity in induction of reaction wood does appear to be through redistribution of auxin moving down the stem from above. Thus again, gravity modifies the normal correlative effect of auxin. Again, also, the gravity effect is a feedback regulation because reaction wood tends to straighten the stem, thus reducing the gravity effect and in turn the stimulus to form more reaction wood.

The last class of interrelationships is the competitive. One example is the competition between the root and the shoot system that can be expressed in terms of the ratio of root system weight to shoot system weight (root-shoot ratio). It is clearly to the best interests of the plant to maintain a root–shoot ratio such that the shoot is adequately supplied with water and minerals by the root. Thus, root growth occurs essentially by robbing photosynthate from shoot growth. Presumably growing roots act as a sink for translocation of materials from the shoots. It is probably significant that there appear to be two peaks of root growth, before and after shoot growth, so that root growth does not always compete directly with shoot growth. The initiation of the growth that creates the sinks is probably due to growth regulators and here the fact that roots appear to be able to produce their own regulators becomes important again because it permits the roots to grow independently of the shoots thus reducing the amount of direct competition between roots and shoots.

There is also competition within the shoot system and within the root system. The generalization appears to be that "the rich get rich and the poor get poorer." The large, faster growing branches or roots are bigger sinks and thus can outcompete smaller, slower growing organs for available photosynthate. Again, the creation of the sink is due to growth and that is in turn due to regulators and may be subject to correlative interactions. Long-shoots grow longer, have more cambial activity and more leaves than the correlatively inhibited short-shoots. Large diameter lateral root tips seem to form when the influence of the main root tip is reduced or eliminated. Once formed these large tips elongate faster and have more cambial activity than small root tips, presumably because they are larger sinks.

Mutual shading by leaves and competition for water by roots are examples of direct competition. If one leaf is above another, the lower one is shaded so that it is at a competitive disadvantage. Two roots growing in the same area are competing for the same water. Roots even exude many substances into the soil and some of these exudates might competitively inhibit the growth of nearby tips.

Notes

1. Introduction

1. One direct use of trees in the study of history is the technique of "dendrochronology" developed at the Tree Ring Laboratory in Arizona. This technique utilizes the fact that tree ring widths and structure reflect annual environmental conditions—particularly in areas where growth is marginal and the trees more responsive to environmental changes. By cross referencing rings from trees of known age with archeological timber remains it is often possible to date the remains with great accuracy. The *Tree Ring Bulletin* contains numerous references on techniques of dendrochronology.

2. What is a Tree?

1. Information on the evolution and variation of tree forms is scattered throughout the literature in plant morphology and paleobotany. BARGHOORN (1964) has treated some aspects of the evolution of trees, particularly the evolution of lignin that is so important in the stiffening of large stems. Other information or an introduction to specific literature can be gleaned from textbooks on plant morphology, such as FOSTER and GIFFORD (1959), or on paleobotany, such as DARRAH (1960). BARGHOORN, E. S. 1964. "Evolution of cambium in geologic time." In *Formation of Wood in Forest Trees* (M. H. Zimmermann, ed.), 3–18, Academic Press, New York. DARRAH, W. C. 1960. *Principles of Paleobotany.* 2nd Edition. Ronald Press, New York. FOSTER, A. S. and E. M. GIFFORD. 1959. *Comparative Morphology of Vascular Plants.* W. H. Freeman and Company, San Francisco.

2. A recent review of the hypotheses about the mechanisms of the geotropic response is: WILKINS, M. W. 1966. Geotropism. *Ann. Rev. Plant Phys.* 17:379–408. CORNER, E. J. H. 1966. *The Natural History of Palms.* University of California Press, Berkeley.

3. See: TOMLINSON, P. B. 1964. "Stem structure in arborescent monocotyledons." In *Formation of Wood in Forest Trees* (M. H. Zimmermann,

ed.), 65–86. Academic Press, New York. The tree ferns are predominantly in the family Cyatheaceae, with some in the Dicksoniaceae. Details of vegetative structure can be found in: BOWER, F. O. 1923. *The Ferns.* Cambridge University Press, London.

4. There are a great many books on water and water relations because it is such a key aspect of plant growth. These books range upwards in difficulty to those (SLATYER, 1967) that take a physical chemistry approach to water relations. Some good examples are: KRAMER, P. J. 1969. *Plant and Soil-water Relationships.* 2nd Edition. McGraw-Hill Book Company, Inc., New York. SLATYER, P. O. 1967. *Plant-water Relationships.* Academic Press, New York. SUTCLIFFE, J. 1968. *Plants and Water.* St. Martin's Press, New York. Some specific aspects of water movement and phloem transport of sugars in trees are covered in most of the books on trees listed under Sources at the end of this book. In addition an interesting article is: ZIMMERMANN, M. H. 1963. "How sap moves in trees." *Sci. Amer.* 208:133–142.

5. A fascinating and well-illustrated book that shakes our preconceived notions of tree growth and form is: MENNINGER, E. A. 1967. *Fantastic Trees.* Viking Press, New York.

3. General Aspects of the Growth Process

1. There are numerous modern references on plant biochemistry and cell biology. Most plant physiology textbooks are slanted in this direction. A thorough treatment is given in: BONNER, J. and J. E. VARNER. 1965. *Plant Biochemistry.* Academic Press, New York. Only three types of modifications to this general model are needed to make models for the major meristems in trees. (1) Apical meristems, both shoot and root, produce new meristems that produce lateral roots or shoots. Shoot apical meristems also produce meristems that develop into leaves. These new meristems which originate laterally, on the side of the parent organ, become the apical meristems of the new lateral roots and shoots. (2) Both root apical meristems and the cambium produce cells in two different directions. The root apical meristem produces root cap cells to the front of the root (they serve to protect the delicate meristem as it pushes through the soil), and the cells that contribute most to the elongation of the root are contributed behind the meristem. The cambium meristem produces wood cells

toward the inside of the tree (xylem cells) and cells specialized for transport of photosynthate (phloem cells) toward the outside. (3) A major difference between apical meristems and the cambium that is not reflected in the models, but that would be easy to add, is that enlargement is primarily through elongation in apical meristems and through radial enlargement in width in the cambium.

2. The concept and operation of plant meristems is well presented in: ESAU, K. 1965. *Plant Anatomy.* 2nd Edition. John Wiley and Sons.

3. The analysis of growth rings has been used as a research tool for well over a century in investigating the effects of silvicultural treatments and environmental conditions on cambial activity. It has been emphasized that there are three different ways to analyze growth rings, the so-called "Duff and Nolan sequences" (DUFF, G. H. and N. J. NOLAN. 1953, 1957. "Growth and morphogenesis in the Canadian forest species. I., II." *Can. J. Botany* 31:471–513, 35:527–572). In the first sequence the width of one growth sheath follows a characteristic pattern from the top to the bottom of the tree with the widest portion usually near the base of the crown. This sequence shows that ring width is a function of distance from the crown. In the second sequence the ring width from pith to bark at any one level also follows a pattern that merely reflects the changing distance from any level in the tree to the base of the crown over the life of the tree. The third sequence is from top to bottom of the tree, but always measuring a ring the same number of rings from the pith. This sequence attempts to eliminate the variable of distance from the crown and thus does not reflect the inherent pattern of ring width. This last sequence is the most useful for studying the effect of environmental conditions during particular years on the amount of cambial activity.

4. Seed dormancy seems extremely complex because each species has different requirements for overcoming dormancy. AMEN, R. D. 1968. "A model of seed dormancy." *Bot. Rev.* 34:1–31, has shown how these varying requirements may all fit together into one generalized system for seed dormancy. ANONYMOUS. 1948. "Woody plant seed manual." *U.S. Forest Service Misc. Publ.* 654. HEIT, C. E. 1968. "Thirty-five years testing of tree and shrub seed." J. FORESTRY. 66:632–634.

5. The problem of juvenility and adolescence is of particular importance to orchardists and tree breeders who want trees to flower as early as possible. With fruit trees, flowering is often hastened by

grafting shoots on to dwarfing rootstocks. It has been suggested that perhaps dwarfing rootstocks produce less gibberellin than normal root stocks (JONES, O. P. and H. J. LACEY. 1968. "Gibberellin-like substances in the transpiration stream of apple and pear trees." *J. Exper. Bot.* 19:526–531). Interference with phloem transport by girdling or strangling also may reduce the time to flowering. Some other aspects of juvenility and adolescence in trees are considered in: SCHAFFALITSKY DE MUCKADELL, M. 1962. "Environmental factors in developmental stages of trees." In *Tree Growth* (T. T. Kozlowski, ed.), pp. 289–297. Ronald Press, New York.

6. Discussions of ageing may be found in: SAX, K: 1962. "Aspects of ageing in plants." *Ann. Rev. Plant Phys.* 13:489–506. WESTING, A. H. 1964. "The longevity and ageing of trees." *The Gerontologist* 4:10–15.

7. There are some beautiful pictures of bristlecone pines, and many other trees in: FEININGER, A. E. 1968. *Trees.* Viking Press, New York.

4. Form of the Branch and Root System

1. WARD, H. M. 1909. *Trees.* Vol. V. Form and Habit. Cambridge University Press, Cambridge.

2. There are many books that treat the various aesthetic and horticultural characteristics of trees with reference to ornamental planting. One especially good book is: WYMAN, O. 1965. *Trees for American Gardens.* 2nd. Edition. MacMillan, New York. A particularly striking place to investigate tree form is at an arboretum where many diverse forms from all over the world are planted in close proximity.

3. TURRELL, F. M. 1961. "Growth of the photosynthetic area of citrus." *Bot. Gaz.* 122:284–298. Turrell measured trees from 3 to 29 years old. An example of his results is that the relationship between total leaf area (A) and tree age(a) for Valencia orange trees could be represented by the allometric equation $A = 9.870a^{1.068}$. The "allometric coefficient," in this case 1.068' was different for different species.

4. WILSON, B. F. 1966. "Development of the shoot system of *Acer rubrum* L." *Harvard Forest Paper No.* 14.

5. BROWN, C. L., R. G. MCALPINE and P. P. KORMANIK. 1967. "Apical dominance and form in woody plants: a reappraisal." *Amer. J. Bot.* 54:153–162.

6. Numerous observations on the growth of conifer roots can be found in the following references: WILCOX, H. 1962. "Growth studies of the root of incense cedar, *Libocedrus decurrens*. II." *Amer. J. Bot.* 49:237–245. ———. 1964. "Xylem in roots of *Pinus resinosa* Ait. in relation to heterorhizy and growth activity." In *Formation of Wood in Forest Trees* (M. H. Zimmermann, ed.), pp. 459–478. Academic Press, New York. ———. 1968. Morphological studies of the root of red pine, *Pinus resinosa*. I. Amer. J. Bot. 55:247–254.

7. The formation of multilayered root systems in spruce after silt deposition is discussed in WAGG, J. W. B. 1967. "Origin and development of white spruce root forms." *Canada Forest Res. Branch Publ. No.* 1192.

5. Elongation and Dormancy of the Branches and Roots

1. RUDOLPH, T. D. 1964. "Lammas growth and prolepsis in jack pine in the Lake States." *Forest Science Monograph* 6. KOZLOWSKI, T. T. 1964. "Shoot growth in woody plants." *Bot. Rev.* 30:335–392.

2. GUNCKEL, J. E. and K. V. THIMANN. 1949. "Studies of development in long shoots and short shoots of *Ginkgo biloba*. III," "IV" (with R. H. WETMORE). *Amer. J. Bot.* 36:145–151, 309–318. BROWN, C. L. 1964. "The seedling habit of longleaf pine." *Georgia Forest Research Council (Monograph)*. Longleaf pine is especially interesting because the seedlings pass through a "grass" stage where even the terminal grows like a short-shoot for 5 or more years. The long needles on these seedlings look somewhat like grass.

3. SACHS, T. and K. V. THIMANN. 1967. "The role of auxins and cytokinins in the release of buds from dominance." *Amer. J. Bot.* 54:136–144. Suggest that the auxin from the main shoot can regulate auxin production in lateral shoots—if the lateral is growing relatively slowly. See also the auxin determinations in: BROWN, C. L., R. G. MCALPINE, and P. P. KORMANIK. 1967. "Apical dominance and form in woody plants: A reappraisal." *Amer. J. Bot.* 54:153–162.

4. See: KOZLOWSKI, T. T. (note 1), and KOZLOWSKI, T. T. and KELLER. 1966. "Food relations of woody plants." *Bot. Rev.* 32:293–382. Both these references are somewhat encyclopedic, but contain many specific references. TEPPER, H. B. 1967. "The role of storage products and

current photosynthate in the growth of which ash seedlings." *Forest Sci.* 13:319–320. This is one of the few studies on nonconiferous species.

5. See note 5, chapter 2, for references on water relations. The Zimmermann reference is especially pertinent because Dr. Zimmermann originally gave me most of the ideas in the discussion of water stress.

6. FIELDING, J. M. 1955. "The seasonal and daily elongation of the shoots of Monterey pine and the daily elongation of the roots." *Forestry and Timber Bureau, Australia, Leaflet No.* 75. HEAD, G. C. 1965. "Studies of diurnal changes in cherry root growth and nutational movements of apple root tips by time-lapse cinematography." *Ann. Bot.* 29:219–224.

7. A number of growth regulators have been isolated from the xylem sap of trees and other woody plants. During periods of active transpiration it is assumed that these substances are formed by the roots. BOWEN, M. R. and G. V. HOAD. 1968. "Inhibitor content of phloem and xylem sap obtained from willow entering dormancy." *Planta* 81:64–70. JONES, O. P. and H. J. LACEY. 1968. "Gibberellin-like substances in the transpiration stream of apple and pear trees." *J. Exp. Bot.* 19:526–531. SKENE, K. G. M. and G. M. KERRIDGE. 1967. "Effect of temperature on cytokinin activity in root exudate of *Vitis vinifera*." *Plant Phys.* 42:1131–1139.

8. ELIASSON, L. 1968. "Dependence of root growth on photosynthesis in *Populus*." *Phys. Plantarum* 21:806–810. RICHARDSON, S. D. 1953. "Studies of root growth in *Acer saccharinum* L. I. The relation between root growth and photosynthesis." *Proc. Koninkl. Akad. v Wetenschap.* Amsterdam C56:346–353. LYR, H. and G. HOFFMAN. 1967. "Growth rates and growth periodicity of tree roots." *International Review of Forestry Research* 2:181–236. LYFORD, W. H. and B. F. WILSON. 1966. "Controlled growth of forest tree roots: technique and applications." *Harvard Forest Paper* No. 16.

9. LOGAN, K. T. 1965, 1966. "Growth of tree seedlings as affected by light intensity. I White birch, yellow birch, sugar maple and silver maple. II. Red pine, white pine, jack pine and eastern larch. III Basswood and white elm." *Canada Dept. of Forestry Publ.* 1121, 1160, 1176. SIMS, H. P. 1964. "Root development of jack pine seedlings on burned over dry sites in southeastern Manitoba." *Canada Dept. of Forestry Publ.* 1061. LOGAN presents data on shoot and root weights that can be converted to shoot:root ratios. SIMS presents the shoot:root ratio for

jack pine seedlings from 1 to 8 years old, plus accurate diagrams of their root systems.

10. See Romberger's book (under sources) for an extensive review of dormancy in roots and shoots.

11. EAGLES, C. G. and P. F. WAREING, 1964. "The role of growth substances in the regulation of bud dormancy." *Phys. Plantarum* 17:697–709.

12. WILCOX, H. E. 1968. "Morphological studies of the root of red pine, *Pinus resinosa*. I. Growth patterns and characteristics of branching." *Amer. J. Bot.* 55:247–254.

6. Lateral Formation and Apical Dominance

1. BROWN, C. L., R. G. MCALPINE, and P. P. KORMANIK. 1967. "Apical dominance and form in woody plants: a reappraisal." *Amer. J. Bot.* 54:153–162. This paper shows several photographs of sylleptic shoots, where laterals grow out in the year they were formed, and point at the important differences between apical *dominance* and apical *control*. WILSON, B. F. 1968. "Red maple stump sprouts: development the first year." *Harvard Forest Paper* No. 18.

2. HASSIG. B. E. 1965. "Organ formation *in vitro* as applicable to forest tree propagation." *Bot. Rev.* 31:607–620. Contains numerous references including the historical development of the technique.

3. WENT, F. W. and K. V. THIMANN. 1937. *Phytohormones*. Macmillan Co., New York.

4. FARMER, R. W., JR. 1961. "Aspen root sucker formation and apical dominance." *Forest Sci.* 8:403–410. MAINI, J. S. and R. W. HORTON. 1966. "Vegetative propagation of *Populus* spp. I. Influence of temperature on formation and initial growth of aspen suckers." *Can. J. Bot.* 44:1183–1189. KORMANIK, P. P. and C. L. BROWN. 1967. "Root buds and development of root suckers in sweetgum." *Forest Sci.* 13:338–345.

5. SACHS, T. and K. V. THIMANN. 1967. "The role of auxins and cytokinins in the release of buds from dominance." *Amer. J. Bot.* 54:136–144.

6. CHAMPAGNAT, P. 1961. "Dominance apicale. Tropisms. Epinastie." *Encycl. Plant Physiol.* 14:872–908.

7. See: BROWN et al. note 1 above. WILSON, B. F. 1966. "Development of the shoot system of *Acer rubrum* L." *Harvard Forest Paper* No. 10. GUNCKEL, J. E., K. V. THIMANN and R. H. WETMORE. 1949. "Studies of

development in long-shoots and short-shoots of *Gingko biloba* L. IV. Growth habit, shoot expression, and the mechanism of its control." *Amer. J. Bot.* 36:309–316. GREGORY, F. G. and J. A. VEALE. 1957. "A reassessment of the problem of apical dominance." *Symp. Soc. Exptl. Biol.* 11:1–20.

8. For a general review see: GOLDSMITH, M. H. M. 1968. "The transport of auxin." *Ann. Rev. Pl. Physiol.* 19:347–360. The specific problem in roots is reviewed in KIRK, S. C. and W. P. JACOBS. 1968. "Polar movement of indole–3–acetic acid–^{14}C in roots of *Lens* and *Phaseolus*." *Plant Physiol.* 43:675–682.

9. A general reference on propagating techniques is HARTMANN, H. T. and D. E. KESTER. 1968. *Plant propagation: Principles and Practices.* Prentice-Hall. Englewood Cliffs, N.J.

10. ZIMMERMANN, M. H., A. B. WARDROP, and P. B. TOMLINSON. 1968. Tension wood in aerial roots of *Ficus benjamin* L." *Wood Sci. and Tech.* 2:95–104. This species of fig has large aerial roots that are usually unbranched in the air, but branch profusely when they reach the soil. Also, once in the soil, they produce a ring of tension wood that actually pulls down the branch to which they are attached.

11. WILCOX, H. E. 1968. "Morphological studies of the root of red pine, *Pinus resinosa*. I. Growth characteristics and patterns of branching." *Amer. J. Bot.* 55:247–254. LYFORD, W. H. and B. F. WILSON. 1964. "Development of the root system of *Acer rubrum* L." *Harvard Forest Paper* No. 10.

12. TORREY, J. G. 1950. "The induction of lateral roots by indoleacetic acid and root decapitation." *Amer. J. Bot.* 37:257–264. RICHARDSON, S. D. 1957. "Bud dormancy and root development in *Acer saccharinum*." In *The Physiology of Forest Trees* (K. V. Thimann, ed.) Ronald Press, New York.

13. TORREY, J. G. 1962. "Auxin and purine interactions in lateral root initiation in isolated pea root segments." *Physiol. Plantarum.* 15:177–185.

7. Orientation of Laterals

1. RUFELT, H. 1961. "Geotropism in roots and shoots." *Ann. Rev. Pl. Physiol.* 12:409–430. BRIGGS, W. R. 1963. "The phototropic responses of higher plants." *Ann. Rev. Pl. Phys.* 14:311–352.

2. WESTING, A. H. 1965, 1968. "The formation and function of compression wood in Gymnosperms. I., II." *Bot. Rev.* 31:381–480, 34:51–105. WARDROP, A. B. 1964. "The reaction anatomy of arborescent angiosperms." In *The Formation of Wood in Forest Trees* (M. H. Zimmermann, ed.), pp. 405–456. Academic Press, N.Y.

3. MÜNCH, E. 1938. "Untersuchungen über die harmonie der baumgestalt." *Jahr. Wiss. Bot.* 86:581–673. Available in English translation from Translation Center, John Crerar Library, 35 West 33rd St. Chicago, Ill. 60616 See WARDROP, note 2 above.

4. MCQUILKIN, W. E. 1935. "Root development of pitch pine with some comparative observations on shortleaf pine." *J. Agr. Res.* 51:983–1016. FAYLE, O. C. F. 1968. "Radial growth in tree roots." *Univ. of Toronto, Faculty of Forestry, Tech. Report No. 9.* The wood of vertical roots is different from the wood of horizontal roots. This suggests that the hormonal environment of the verticals is different.

5. WILSON, B. F. 1967. "Root growth around barriers." *Bot. Gaz.* 128:79–82.

8. The Process of Cambial Activity

1. For a review of various types of anomalous cambial activity see: PHILIPSON, W. R. and J. M. WARD. 1965. "The ontogeny of the vascular cambium in the stems of seed plants." *Biol. Reviews* 40:534–579.

2. Cambial activity in conifers has been studied enough to make a quantitative model of the process. See: WILSON, B. F. and R. A. HOWARD. 1968. "A computer model for cambial activity." *Forest Science* 14:77–90. A good deal of the following discussion is based on the model presented in this paper.

3. There are numerous books on wood anatomy. Identification of many woods can be done with a hand lens, but identification of others, like the coniferous species, has to be done with a microscope. See: BROWN, H. P., A. J. PANSHIN, and C. C. FORSAITH. 1949. *Textbook of Wood Technology*. Volume 1. McGraw-Hill Book Co., New York.

4. It is easiest to visualize the course of vessels in this three-dimensional network in movies made from serial cross sections of the wood. See: ZIMMERMANN, M. H. and P. B. TOMLINSON. 1967. "A method for the analysis of the course of vessels." *Bull. Int. Assoc. Wood Anatomists* 1:2–6.

5. Many of Bailey's classic papers are collected in the book. BAILEY, I. W. 1954. *Contributions to Plant Anatomy.* Chronica Botanica Co., Waltham.

6. One of the recent of the many papers that have appeared in the *Canadian Journal of Botany* is: BANNAN, M. W. 1966. "Spiral grain and anticlinal divisions in the cambium of conifers." *Can. J. Bot.* 44:1515–1538.

7. Some excellent studies on the ontogeny and phylogeny of rays are: BARGHOORN, E. S., JR. 1940. "Origin and development of the uniseriate ray in the coniferææ *Torrey Bot. Club Bull.* 67:303–328. _____. 1940, 1941. "The ontogenetic development and phylogenetic specialization of rays in the xylem of dicotyledons. I., II., III." *Amer. J. Bot.* 27:918–928, 28:273–282. *Torrey Bot. Club Bull.* 68:317–325.

8. See note 2 in the previous chapter.

9. WATANABE, H. 1967. "A study of the origin of longitudinal growth stresses in tree stems." *Bull. Kyushu Univ. For.* 41:169–176.

9. Regulation of Cambial Activity

1. DIGBY, J. and P. F. WAREING. 1966. "The relationship between endogenous hormone levels in the plant and seasonal aspects of cambial activity." *Ann. Bot.* 30:607–622.

2. GREGORY, R. A. and B. F. WILSON. 1968. "A comparison of cambial activity of white spruce in Alaska and New England." *Can. J. Bot.* 46:733–734.

3. DIGBY and WAREING, note 1 above. LARSON, P. R. 1964. "Some indirect effects of environment on wood formation." In *Formation of Wood in Forest Trees* (M. H. Zimmermann, ed.) pp. 345–365. Academic Press, New York. WAISEL, Y. and A. FAHN. 1965. "The effects of environment on wood formation and cambial activity in *Robinia pseudoaceacia* L." *New Phyt.* 64:436–442.

4. LARSON, P. R. 1965. "Stem form of young *Larix* as influenced by wind and pruning." *Forest Science* 11:412–424.

5. DOLEY, D. and L. LEIGHTON. 1968. "Effects of growth regulating substances and water potential on the development of secondary xylem in *Fraxinus.*" *New Phytol.* 67:579–594. LARSON, note 3 above. DIGBY, J. and P. F. WAREING. 1966. "The effect of applied growth hor-

mones on cambial division and the differentiation of the cambial derivatives." *Ann. Bot.* 30:539–548. SHEPHERD, K. R. 1964. "Some observations on the effect of drought on the growth of *Pinus radiata* D. Don." *Australian For.* 28:1–22.

6. LARSON, note 3 above. DOLEY and LEIGHTON, note 5 above.

7. RICHARDSON, S. D. 1964. "The external environment and tracheid size in conifers." In *The Formation of Wood in Forest Trees* (M. H. Zimmermann, ed.) pp. 367–388. Academic Press, New York. GORDON, J. C. and P. R. LARSON. 1968. "Seasonal course of photosynthesis, respiration, and distribution of ^{14}C in young *Pinus resinosa* trees as related to wood formation." *Plant Physiol.* 43:1617–1624.

8. WHITMORE, F. W. and R. ZAHNER. 1966. "Development of the xylem ring in stems of young red pine trees." *Forest Science* 12:198–210. WODZICKI, T. J. 1965. "Annual ring of wood formation and seasonal changes of natural growth inhibitors in larch." *Acta Soc. Bot. Poloniae* 34:117–151.

9. See note 2, chapter 7 on Orientation. SINNOTT, E. W. 1952. "Reaction wood and the regulation of tree form." *Amer. J. Bot.* 39:69–78. KENNEDY, R. W. and J. L. FARRAR. 1965. "Tracheid development in tilted seedlings." In *Cellular Ultrastructure of Woody Plants.* (W. Coté, ed.) p. 419–453. Syracuse University Press, Syracuse, N.Y.

10. Distribution Problems

1. LARSON, P. R. 1964. "Stem form development of forest trees." *Forest Science Monograph* No. 5. A comprehensive review of the several theories to explain stem form.

2. FARRAR, J. L. 1961. Longitudinal variation in the thickness of the annual ring." *For. Chron.* 37:323–330. FAYLE, D. C. F. 1968. "Radial growth in tree roots." *University of Toronto, Faculty of Forestry, Tech. Rep. No. 9.*

3. See: MÜNCH, note 3 in chapter 7 for experiments on disbudding pine trees.

4. See: LARSON, note 4, chapter 9 on regulation of cambial activity.

5. I gratefully acknowledge the contributions of Mr. Alan Page in developing the ideas for this discussion of branch angle.

11. Growth of the Whole Tree

1. A general treatment of plant organ and tissue culture, plus other aspects of plant development may be found in: TORREY, J. G. 1967. "Development in flowering plants." MacMillan Company, New York. Also see: BROWN, C. L. 1964. "The influence of external pressure on the differentiation of cells and tissues cultured *in vitro*." In *The Formation of Wood in Forest Trees* (M. H. Zimmermann, ed.) pp. 389–404. Academic Press, New York.

Sources

Books for General Reference about Trees

BÜSGEN, M. and E. MÜNCH. 1931. *The Structure and Life of Forest Trees.* 3rd Edition. John Wiley and Sons, Inc., New York.

FOWELLS, H. A. 1965. *Silvics of Forest Trees of the United States.* USDA Agricultural Handbook No. 271.

KOZLOWSKI, T. T. (ed.) 1962. *Tree Growth.* Ronald Press, New York.

KRAMER, P. J. and T. T. KOXLOWSKI. 1960. *Physiology of Trees.* McGraw-Hill Book Company, New York.

ROMBERGER, J. A. 1963. *Meristems, Growth and Development in Woody Plants.* U.S. Dept. of Agric. Tech. Bull. No. 1293.

THIMANN, K. V. (ed.). 1958. *The Physiology of Forest Trees.* Ronald Press, New York.

ZIMMERMANN, M. H. (ed.) 1964. *The Formation of Wood in Forest Trees.* Academic Press, New York.

Books for General Reference about Plant Growth

ESAU, K. 1965. *Plant Anatomy.* 2nd Edition. John Wiley and Sons, New York.

LEOPOLD, A. C. 1964. *Plant Growth and Development.* McGraw-Hill Book Company, New York.

SALISBURY, F. B. and C. ROSS. 1969. *Plant Physiology.* Wadsworth Publishing Co., Belmont, Calif.

SINNOT, E. W. 1960. *Plant Morphogenesis.* McGraw-Hill Book Company, New York.

Serial Review Publications of Interest

Annual Reviews of Plant Physiology. 1951+
Encyclopedia of Plant Physiology. 18 volumes. 1955–1967.
Botanical Review. 1931+

Scientific articles on tree growth are scattered through scores of Forestry and Botany journals. A good way to locate articles on specific subjects is to use *Forestry Abstracts* or *Biological Abstracts*.

Index